THE PHYSICS OF GLACIERS

THE PHYSICS OF
GLACIERS

by

W. S. B. PATERSON

THE QUEEN'S AWARD
TO INDUSTRY 1966

PERGAMON PRESS

OXFORD · LONDON · EDINBURGH · NEW YORK
TORONTO · SYDNEY · PARIS · BRAUNSCHWEIG

Pergamon Press Ltd., Headington Hill Hall, Oxford
4 & 5 Fitzroy Square, London W.1

Pergamon Press (Scotland) Ltd., 2 & 3 Teviot Place, Edinburgh 1

Pergamon Press Inc., Maxwell House, Fairview Park, Elmsford,
New York 10523

Pergamon of Canada Ltd., 207 Queen's Quay West, Toronto 1

Pergamon Press (Aust.) Pty. Ltd., 19a Boundary Street,
Rushcutters Bay, N.S.W. 2011, Australia

Pergamon Press S.A.R.L., 24 rue des Écoles, Paris 5ᵉ

Vieweg & Sohn GmbH, Burgplatz 1, Braunschweig

First edition 1969

Library of Congress Catalog Card No. 71–82909

Printed in Hungary

08 013971 x (flexicover)
08 013972 8 (hard cover)

CONTENTS

Contents

PREFACE

THE aim of this book is to explain the physical principles underlying the behaviour of glaciers and ice sheets, as far as these are understood at the present time.

Glaciers have been studied scientifically for more than a century. During this period, interest in the subject has, like the glaciers themselves, waxed and waned. Periods of activity and advance have alternated with periods of stagnation and even of retrogression when erroneous ideas have become part of the conventional wisdom. The past 20 years, however, have seen a major advance in our knowledge. Theories have been developed which have explained many facts previously obscure; improved observational techniques have enabled these theories to be tested and have produced new results still to be explained.

This seems an appropriate time to review these recent developments. At present there is, to my knowledge, no book in English which does this. The present book is a modest attempt to fill the gap. To cover the whole field in a short book is impossible. I have tried to select those topics which I feel to be of most significance; but there is undoubtedly some bias towards my own particular interests.

While the book is intended primarily for those starting research in the subject, I hope that established workers in glacier studies, and in related fields, will find it useful. The treatment is at about the graduate student level. The standard varies, however, and most chapters should be intelligible to senior undergraduates.

I am much indebted to Dr. J. F. Nye for reading the whole manuscript and making many helpful suggestions. I am grateful to Drs. S. J. Jones, G. de Q. Robin and J. Weertman for reviewing individual chapters. I should also like to thank Drs. J. A.

Jacobs and J. Tuzo Wilson for general comments and encouragement. The responsibility for the final form and contents of the book of course remains my own.

Ottawa, Canada W. S. B. PATERSON

CHAPTER 1

INTRODUCTION

GLACIER ice covers some 10 per cent of the earth's land surface at the present time and covered about three times as much during the ice ages. However, at present, all but about 4 per cent of this ice is in areas remote from man's normal activities, the great ice sheets of Greenland and Antarctica. Thus it is not surprising that the relatively small glaciers in mountain areas were the first to attract attention.

Descriptions of glaciers can be found in 11th century Icelandic literature, but the fact that they move doesn't appear to have been noticed, or at any rate recorded, until some 500 years later. Since that time, the problem of how a large, apparently solid, mass of ice can flow has been studied and debated by many eminent scientists. Altmann, in 1751, correctly recognized that gravity was the cause of glacier motion, but he thought that movement consisted entirely of the ice sliding over its bed. Many glaciers do slide in this way but, in addition, the ice itself can flow, somewhat like a very viscous fluid, as Bordier suggested in the late 18th century. In 1849 Thomson demonstrated ice flow in the laboratory though the interpretation of his experiment later caused some confusion. Forbes asserted that glacier movement was viscous flow, but Tyndall opposed this view. He thought that motion resulted from the formation of numerous small fractures that were subsequently healed by pressure melting and refreezing. The resulting controversy, as Seligman has remarked, generated enough heat to melt a small glacier. A proper understanding of the mechanism of glacier flow has been reached only in the past 20 years, by the application of modern ideas in solid state physics and metallurgy. This followed the realization that, as ice is a crystalline solid, it should deform like other crystalline solids such as metals, at temperatures near their melting points.

Systematic measurements on glaciers were begun about 1830 in the Alps. The aim of most early measurements was to find out how movement varies from place to place on a glacier. Agassiz showed that the velocity is greatest in the central part and decreases progressively towards each side. He also found that a glacier moves more slowly near its head and terminus than elsewhere. Reid, in 1897, showed that the velocity vectors are not parallel to the glacier surface. They are inclined slightly downwards in the higher parts of the glacier, where snow accumulates, and slightly upwards in the lower reaches to compensate for ice lost by melting.

Other developments about the turn of the century were the observation by Vallot of what would now be called a kinematic wave moving down the Mer de Glace, the observation of seasonal variations in velocity, and the development of mathematical models of glacier flow by Finsterwalder and others. Finsterwalder also pioneered photogrammetric methods of mapping glaciers.

Ice movement at depth was long the subject of debate. Does the deep ice really move faster than ice near the surface, as many geology textbooks still assert? In the early 1900's Blümcke and Hess used a thermal drill in a glacier in the Tyrol and attained bedrock in eleven holes, one of them more than 200 m deep. Rods left in the holes gradually tilted downhill. This suggested that the surface ice moves more rapidly than the ice at depth, a fact confirmed by recent, more sophisticated, borehole measurements.

The ice sheets of Greenland and Antarctica present special problems. These ice sheets seem able to maintain themselves, although precipitation on them is as low as in desert areas of the world. How would a change in climate alter their thickness and extent? How does snow turn into ice when there is no melting? How old is the ice at different depths? What can an examination of such ice tell us about the climate at the time it was deposited as snow? Study of the flow of existing ice sheets helps us understand the behaviour of the ice sheets which covered much of northern Europe and North America during the ice ages. It also helps us to interpret the deposits which these ice sheets left behind and helps us to assess the many theories which have been proposed to account for the ice ages.

Noteworthy early work on polar ice sheets is Koch and Wegener's study of snow stratigraphy during their crossing of Greenland in 1913. Koch and Wegener also measured temperatures in the ice, in one instance down to a depth of 24 m. Wegener's Greenland Expedition of 1930-1, which wintered in the central part of the ice sheet, studied the way in which snow is transformed to ice. They also made seismic measurements of ice thickness, a method first tried a few years earlier in the Alps.

That glaciers advance and retreat in response to changes in climate is common knowledge; but the relationship is much more complex than is usually assumed. Ahlmann, between 1920 and 1940, carried out classic investigations on this subject on glaciers in Scandinavia, Spitsbergen, Iceland and Greenland. Complementary studies of how a glacier surface receives heat during the melting season were begun by Sverdrup in Spitsbergen in 1934. But an understanding of the meteorological problems is not enough: the flow characteristics of each particular glacier determines how it will react to a climatic change. The past few years have seen impressive theoretical developments in this second aspect of the problem, so that now the prime need is for more, or rather, better data.

This brief historical review indicates some steps in the development of the subject and some of the topics we shall discuss. Hopefully, it should also correct any false impression, which may be gained from subsequent chapters, that only in the past 20 years has any significant progress been made in glacier studies.

The review also illustrates the wide range of the subject. Study of glaciers is part of glaciology, the study of ice in all its forms. Glaciology, like other branches of geophysics, is an interdisciplinary subject involving physicists, mathematicians, crystallographers, geologists, meteorologists, climatologists and others. For instance, a joint meeting of glaciologists and metal-lurgists, held in England in 1948, was the beginning of the application to glacier flow of modern ideas about the deformation of crystalline solids.

The approach in this book emphasizes the physics combined where necessary with mathematics. No apology is made for introducing mathematics. In the author's opinion, a mere handful of mathematical physicists, who may seldom set foot on a glacier, have contributed far more to the understanding of the subject than have a hundred measurers of ablation stakes or recorders of advances and retreats of glacier termini. This is not to say that the latter are unimportant: in glaciology, as in other branches of science, there is a place for both the theoretical and the experimental approach. But the two should be coordinated; the experiments designed to investigate specific problems. Too often in the past, glaciological measurements have been made on the premise that the mere acquisition of data is a useful contribution in itself. This is seldom the case.

Further Reading

SHARP, R. P. *Glaciers*. University of Oregon Press, Eugene, Oregon, U.S.A., 1960.
An excellent introduction. Recommended as preliminary reading.
KAMB, B. Glacier geophysics. *Science* **146**, 353, 1964.
An excellent and up-to-date review article.
LLIBOUTRY, L. *Traité de Glaciologie*. Masson, Paris. Vol. 1, 1964 and Vol. 2, 1965.
A comprehensive and detailed work of 1040 pages. The only modern book covering the whole field of glaciology.

CHAPTER 2

THE TRANSFORMATION OF SNOW AND ICE

"This huge ice is, in my opinion, nothing but snow, which... is only
a little dissolved to moisture, whereby it becomes more compact..."
R. FOTHERBY, *The Voyages of William Baffin* (17th century).

Introduction

A fall of snow on a glacier is the first step in the formation of
glacier ice, a process which is often long and complex. As one
might expect, the way in which snow changes to ice, and the time
the transformation takes, depends on the temperature. Snow
develops into ice much more rapidly in glaciers in temperate regions, where periods of melting alternate with periods when the
soaked snow refreezes, than in central Antarctica, where the
temperature remains well below freezing point throughout the
year. Thus we are dealing, not with a single transformation process, but with different processes in different areas. We have to
subdivide glaciers, and even different parts of the same glacier,
into different categories according to the amount of melting that
takes place.

As snow develops into ice, its density steadily increases. Once
the material becomes ice, there is little further change in density;
but the ice can change in other ways. The ice in a moving glacier
is subject to stresses and these can alter the size and orientation
of the ice crystals. While changes of this kind are expected, some
of the particular changes observed in glacier ice are not. They
have not yet been satisfactorily explained.

The best place to examine how ice deforms in response to an
applied stress is in the laboratory. Numerous studies of this kind

have been made. The behaviour of ice is found to be similar in many ways to that of metals, at temperatures not far below their melting points, and can be explained in terms of modern ideas in solid state physics. This laboratory work is relevant to the changes observed in glacier ice, described in the present chapter. It also forms the basis of the theory of the flow of glaciers and ice sheets, developed in Chapters 6 and 9.

We shall first describe the different zones into which a glacier may be divided. The zones differ from each other in the temperature and physical characteristics of the material near the surface. Next we shall deal with the ways in which snow can be transformed to glacier ice. We shall then outline the results of laboratory work on the deformation of ice, especially the mechanism of this deformation and the changes produced in the ice. Finally we describe the stress-induced changes observed in glacier ice.

Snow, Firn, and Ice

The term "snow" is usually restricted to material which has undergone little modification since it fell. Material in the intermediate stages of transformation is called *firn*. The transformation process varies so widely between different areas that it is almost impossible to find a definition of firn which will apply in all cases. We may sometimes speak of "snow" when "firn" would be more appropriate. The problem is to draw the line

TABLE 2.1. TYPICAL DENSITIES (g cm^{-3})

"Wild snow" (new snow at low temperature in calm)	0·01–0·03
New snow (immediately after falling in calm)	0·05–0·07
Damp new snow	0·1 –0·2
Settled snow	0·2 –0·3
Depth hoar	0·2 –0·3
Wind packed snow	0·35–0·4
Firn	0·4 –0·85
Very wet snow and firn	0·7 –0·8
Glacier ice	0·85–0·91

between snow and firn; the line between firn and ice is clear cut. Firn becomes glacier ice when the interconnecting air passages between grains are sealed off. (By "grain" we mean an aggregate of several crystals.) This occurs at a density between 0·8 and 0·85 g cm^{-3}. Glacier ice is impermeable to air and water: air is present only as bubbles.

Table 2.1, taken mainly from a book by Seligman (1936, p. 144), lists the densities of the different materials. The term "depth hoar" will be explained later.

Zones in a Glacier

Ahlmann (1935a) proposed a "geophysical" classification of glaciers according to ice temperature and amount of surface melting. His categories were *temperate*, *sub-polar*, and *high-polar*. (A temperate glacier is at the pressure melting point throughout. There is no surface melting in a high-polar glacier.) Subsequent authors have subdivided some of Ahlmann's classes. However, conditions vary from one point of a glacier to another; very few glaciers can be fitted into a single category. Thus, to speak about different zones in a glacier seems better than trying to classify entire glaciers. The idea of zones was developed by Benson (1961). Müller (1962a) has added further details.

We shall now describe the characteristics of the zones, starting from the head of the glacier. Very few glaciers will show the entire sequence. Moreover, on any glacier the zone boundaries will vary from year to year according to weather conditions. Figure 2.1 shows the features of the different zones.

1. *Dry snow zone.* No melting occurs here, even in summer. The boundary between this zone and the next one is called the *dry snow line*.

2. *Percolation zone.* Some surface melting occurs in this zone. Water can percolate a certain distance into snow at temperatures below 0°C before it refreezes. If the water encounters a relatively impermeable layer it may spread out laterally for some distance. When it refreezes an "ice layer" or an "ice lens" is formed. The vertical water channels also refreeze, when their water

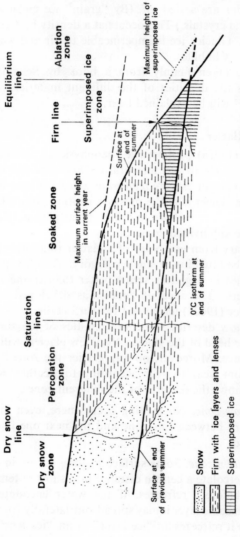

FIG. 2.1. Zones in accumulation area. Based on Müller (1962a).

supply is cut off, to form pipe-like structures called "ice glands". As the freezing of 1 g of water releases enough latent heat to raise the temperature of 160 g of snow by 1 deg, refreezing of meltwater is the most important factor in warming the snow. As summer advances, successively deeper layers of snow are raised to the melting point. The amount of meltwater produced during a summer generally increases with decrease of elevation. Thus, as we go down glacier, we eventually reach a point where, by the end of the summer, all the snow deposited since the end of the previous summer has been raised to the melting temperature. This point, the *saturation line*, is the boundary of the next zone.

3. *Soaked zone.* In this zone, by the end of the summer, all the snow deposited since the end of the previous summer has been raised to 0°C. Some meltwater also percolates into the deeper layers which were deposited in previous years, though not necessarily in sufficient quantity to raise their temperature to 0°C. Percolation into these layers may also occur in the lower part of the percolation zone. It is important to find out where this happens because, when it does, mass balance measurements cannot be restricted to the current year's layer (see Chapter 3). Müller subdivides the soaked zone into two parts, separated by the *slush limit*, the highest point on the glacier at which any material is lost by run-off. The name arises because such run-off often takes the form of slush avalanches.

4. *Superimposed ice zone.* In the percolation and soaked zones, the material consists of ice layers, lenses, and glands, separated by layers and patches of snow or firn. At lower elevations, however, so much meltwater is produced that the ice layers merge to a continuous mass of ice. This is *superimposed ice.* The term "superimposed ice zone" is, however, restricted to the area in which there is an annual increment of superimposed ice exposed at the surface. Superimposed ice is also formed in the lower part of the soaked zone; but there it is buried beneath firn. There is no agreed term for the boundary between the soaked and superimposed ice zones. It has been called the *firn line*, *firn edge* and *annual snow line*. Its location is easily determined:

it is the boundary between firn and ice on the glacier surface at the end of the melt season. The lower boundary of the superimposed ice zone is taken at the *equilibrium line*. This line is important in mass balance studies. Above it, the glacier has a net gain of mass over the year; below it there is a net loss. Some superimposed ice is formed below the equilibrium line, but it is lost by the end of the summer.

5. *Ablation zone*. This is the area below the equilibrium line.

Certain differences in terminology must be explained. The percolation zone as defined here is the same as Benson's percolation zone and Müller's percolation zone A. The soaked zone as defined here corresponds to Benson's soaked zone and is a combination of Müller's percolation zone B and slush zones. Benson includes the superimposed ice zone in the ablation zone.

Distribution of Zones

The only dry snow zones are in the interiors of Greenland and Antarctica. Benson (1961) found that the dry snow zone in Greenland coincides roughly with the region where the mean annual air temperature is −25°C or less. (As we shall see in Chapter 10, the mean annual air temperature in a dry snow zone is equal to the temperature at a depth of 10 m in the firn.) However, Langway (1967) states that, in many summers, a little melting occurs even at the highest elevations in Greenland. Thus the whole sequence of zones may be found in parts of Greenland and Antarctica. On the other hand, the dry snow line on the Filchner Ice Shelf in Antarctica appears to lie about 5 km from the outer edge of the shelf. Thus the ice shelf, and the part of the ice cap which drains into it, is entirely a dry snow zone except for a small percolation zone near the sea. The whole mass loss results from calving of icebergs. The whole sequence, except for a dry snow zone, occurs on some large glaciers in northern Ellesmere Island and Axel Heiberg Island. In cold summers there may be dry snow zones on the highest icefields in these areas. The Barnes Ice Cap in Baffin Island, on the other hand, appears to consist only of superimposed ice and ablation zones in most years. All these are "cold" glaciers, that is, glaciers in which the temperature is below the pressure melting point.

In a "temperate" glacier the ice is at the pressure melting point throughout, except for a surface layer, some 10 m thick, in which the temperature is below 0°C for part of the year. Temperate glaciers cannot have percolation zones because in that zone, by definition, the temperature of part of the current year's snow-pack, and thus also the temperature of deeper layers, never reaches 0°C. Again, superimposed ice only forms if the firn temperature is below 0°C. On a temperate glacier the extent of any superimposed ice zone is insignificant and, for practical purposes, the equilibrium and firn lines coincide. A temperate glacier thus has only soaked and ablation zones. The reverse statement is not necessarily true. Each winter's "cold wave" will normally penetrate through several annual layers in the firn. For a glacier to be temperate the cold wave must be completely eliminated by the end of the summer. For a region to be classified as a soaked zone it is only necessary that the cold wave be eliminated from the current year's snow.

How Snow turns into Ice in a Dry Snow Zone

This subject has been discussed by Shumskiy (1964, pp. 257–76), Anderson and Benson (1963), and Hobbs (1965), among others.

The gradual transformation of snow to glacier ice results from changes in the constituent crystals. We can summarize these as:

(1) Mutual displacement of crystals.
(2) Changes in size and shape.
(3) Internal deformation.

The relative importance of these mechanisms changes as the density of the material increases. The net result, however, is that the crystals grow larger and join together while the air spaces between them are eliminated.

Changes in crystal size and shape occur readily because, unlike other solids, ice is usually at a temperature near its melting point.

Molecules are thus relatively free to move both within the ice lattice ("volume diffusion") and over the crystal surface ("surface diffusion"). In addition, sublimation occurs readily. (The term "sublimation" can be used in two senses. It can be restricted to the change from solid to vapour phase. It is also used to denote the whole sequence of change from solid to vapour, movement of vapour, and change from vapour back to solid. We shall use the word in the latter sense. It is implied that changes between solid and vapour take place without passing through the liquid phase.) At least in the early stages of transformation, sublimation is much more important than either volume or surface diffusion.

The net direction of movement of molecules is governed by the thermodynamic principle that the free energy of the system tends to a minimum. A reduction in surface area reduces the free energy. Thus the molecules tend to be redistributed in a way which reduces the total surface area of the crystals. Thus fresh snowflakes, with their complex shapes, are gradually transformed to spherical particles. Breaking of the snowflakes as they strike the surface, or if they are blown along afterwards, also helps to bring this about. In addition, the larger crystals tend to grow at the expense of the smaller ones as this further reduces the free energy.

However, the most important factor in the initial stages of transformation is settling, that is, the displacement of individual particles relative to their neighbours. The rounding of particles makes this easier. We can estimate the increase in density that settling can bring about, by considering a group of spheres, all of the same size. In what is called the rhombohedral arrangement, which represents the closest possible packing of spheres, the porosity (ratio of space between spheres to total volume) can be shown to be 26 per cent. However, packing experiments with spheres show that, in practice, one can never reduce the porosity below about 40 per cent. For spheres of ice of density 0.91 g cm^{-3} a porosity of 40 per cent corresponds to a density of 0.55 g cm^{-3}. Other mechanisms must be responsible for any further increase in density, so we might expect a decrease in the rate of change of density with time at this point. Observations confirm this as we shall see later.

A packed assembly of spherical particles is not the end result. The total surface area can be further reduced by transfer of material to the points of contact between particles, to form bonds. This process is called *sintering*. Laboratory experiments show that sublimation, rather than diffusion, is the dominant process of mass transfer in the sintering of ice (Hobbs and Mason, 1964).

As the density increases and the firn becomes less porous, sublimation is greatly reduced. At the same time, the load and the area of contact between grains are increasing. (A "grain" may be a single crystal or an aggregate of crystals.) Recrystallization becomes the dominant process: the size and shape of grains change in such a way as to reduce the stresses on them. These changes are brought about by molecular diffusion. In addition, individual crystals deform by movement along internal glide planes.

When the density reaches about 0·8 or 0·85 g cm^{-3}, the air spaces between grains have become closed off. Much of the air has escaped to the surface: the remainder is present only as bubbles in the ice. The firn has now become glacier ice. A further slow increase in density results from compression of the air bubbles.

Most of these processes are sensitive to temperature. Thus the rate of transformation varies from place to place. Differences in accumulation rate contribute to these variations by changing the rate at which the load on a given particle increases with time.

The stresses between neighbouring crystals are continually changing during the transformation process. At low densities, the vertical compressive stress is greater than the horizontal components. However, as the density of the firn approaches that of ice the overall stress pattern becomes approximately hydrostatic. Thus the crystals should be no more likely to grow in one direction than in any other. Examination of ice cores from dry snow zones confirms that the orientation of the crystals is random.

Depth Hoar

In certain circumstances, the transformation of recently-fallen snow proceeds in a way quite different from that previously described. Instead of small round grains, large crystals in the shape of prisms, pyramids, or hollow hexagonal cups are produced. These are called *depth hoar*. This is the most coarse-grained type of firn which can be formed in the absence of meltwater. The average grain size is in the range 2 to 5 mm, but some crystals can be much larger than this. A layer of depth hoar is highly porous and its density is low (0·2 to 0·3 g cm^{-3}). Depth hoar layers are usually only a few centimetres thick. As the name implies, depth hoar is produced within the snowpack, not on the surface.

Depth hoar is formed by sublimation, and can only develop in unconsolidated snow. Conditions seem to be especially favourable when the snow is lying on top of much denser material such as ice. A strong vertical temperature gradient, to produce a strong gradient of vapour pressure, is essential. Such conditions usually occur in autumn when the surface is cooling rapidly and the underlying layers are still relatively warm. Evaporation takes place in the lower layers. The vapour rises and condenses to form depth hoar crystals in the cold upper layers, especially at places where they are relatively impermeable. Some vapour may also escape to the air. Growth of depth hoar crystals represents an increase in the internal energy of the system. This is supplied by the temperature gradient.

In arctic glaciers, a layer of depth hoar is developed each autumn. Depth hoar is easily recognized in the walls of a snow pit and proves very useful for identifying layers for measurements of annual accumulation. Depth hoar can form in any zone when conditions are favourable, but it is destroyed by the following summer's meltwater, except in the dry snow zone and possibly also in the percolation zone,

Transformation when there is Meltwater

We shall now describe briefly how the transformation of snow to ice in the percolation and soaked zones differs from that in the dry snow zone. There is of course a difference only during summer and down to the maximum depth to which meltwater penetrates. Elsewhere, and at other times of year, the processes are the same as in a dry snow zone. Shumskiy (1964, pp. 276–303) has discussed this topic in detail.

Packing of grains is still the most important factor in the initial stages. Melting increases the rate at which grains become rounded, because the grains melt first at their extremities. The average grain size increases because the smaller grains tend to melt before the larger ones. In addition grains may join together in clusters by regelation (refreezing after pressure melting). Joining of grains is particularly rapid in the surface layers because these undergo a daily cycle of freezing and thawing. Meltwater accelerates packing by lubricating the grains, and permits very close packing because the surface tension of a water film tends to pull the grains together. Thus the maximum density which can be attained by packing is higher in a meltwater area than in a dry snow zone.

Refreezing of meltwater also speeds up the later stages of transformation. Air spaces are filled in this way. Refreezing of large quantities of meltwater to form ice layers and lenses represents a rapid transition from snow to ice. The time needed to complete the transformation will vary widely between different areas, according to the amount of meltwater. A superimposed ice zone represents the extreme case in which snow is transformed to ice in a single summer.

Depth–Density Curves

The progress of the transformation of snow to ice at a given place can be shown by a graph of density versus depth. Two such curves, smoothed to some extent, are shown in Fig. 2.2. Langway (1967) made the measurements at Site 2 (latitude 77°N, longitude 56°W) in Greenland. The data for Upper Seward Glacier in the Yukon were obtained by Sharp (1951). Site 2 is near the dry snow line; the other location is in the soaked zone of a temperate glacier. The curve for a percolation zone would lie between these two. The transformation is much more rapid in the soaked zone than in the dry snow zone. Firn becomes ice (density

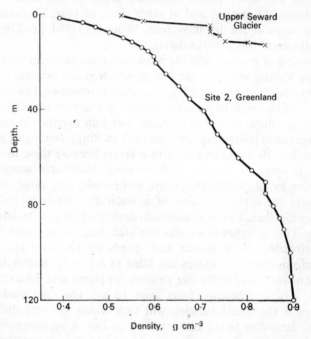

FIG. 2.2. Variation of firn density with depth in a temperate glacier and in the Greenland ice sheet. From Sharp (1951) and Langway (1967).

0.85 g cm^{-3}) at a depth of about 13 m on Seward Glacier but not until a depth of 80 m at Site 2. (In a percolation zone the transition depth is probably between 35 and 75 m.) The difference is even more striking if expressed in terms of time by using the known rate of snow accumulation in each area. Snow is transformed to ice in 3 to 5 years on Upper Seward Glacier: more than 100 years are needed at Site 2.

These curves show certain features predicted in the previous theoretical discussion. The curve for Site 2 can be represented quite well by three straight lines, one for densities less than about 0.58 g cm^{-3}, one in the density range 0.58 to about 0.83 g cm^{-3}, and one for densities above the last value. The value 0.58 g cm^{-3} represents the maximum density which can be attained by packing. The value 0.83 g cm^{-3} represents the point at which the air in the ice has been sealed off in bubbles. The slow increase in density beyond this point is due to compression of the bubbles. The curve for Upper Seward Glacier changes slope at a density of above 0.7 g cm^{-3}. This, the maximum density attained by packing, is greater than the corresponding value for Site 2, as predicted.

Bader (1960, 1963), Anderson and Benson (1963), and Costes (1963) have derived formulae relating density and depth in a dry snow zone. These expressions contain parameters which depend on the physical properties of the firn and whose values have to be determined by laboratory tests. Alternatively, by finding which theoretical curve provides the best fit to a measured depth–density curve, the values of the parameters appropriate to the firn in that particular area can be obtained.

Structure of the Ice Crystal

As a preliminary to discussing the deformation of ice crystals, we shall briefly describe their structure. Further details may be found in the books by Shumskiy (1964, pp. 24–31) and Pounder (1965, pp. 62–85).

First we consider the structure of a molecule of H_2O. The three nuclei of this molecule can be pictured as forming an isosceles triangle with the oxygen nucleus at the apex and the hydrogen nuclei (protons) at the other two corners. The oxygen atom has eight electrons, two of which circle close to the nucleus. Another two rotate in eccentric orbits each of which also contains the electron from one of the hydrogen atoms. Each of these orbits thus encloses the oxygen nucleus and one proton. The remaining four electrons rotate in two other eccentric orbits. The four eccentric orbits radiate tetrahedrally from the oxygen nucleus. The electron orbits completely screen the oxygen nucleus. They do not screen all the positive charge of the protons, however, and they also provide an excess negative charge in the directions of the two orbits without protons. We can thus picture the ice molecule as a regular tetrahedron with positive charges in two corners and negative charges in the other two. Moreover, each negative corner attracts a positive corner in a neighbouring molecule, joining the molecules together by a "hydrogen bond". Thus each molecule is surrounded by four other molecules in a regular tetrahedral arrangement. The spacing between molecules in ice is 2·76 Å.

A substance in which every atom has four neighbours in regular tetrahedral arrangement can crystallize hexagonally or

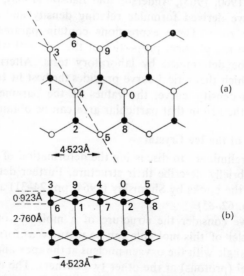

FIG. 2.3. Structure of ice crystal. The circles denote oxygen atoms. The numbers denote corresponding atoms in the two diagrams. (a) Projection of lattice on basal plane. Light and dark circles denote atoms in two planes 0·923 Å apart: the bonds between atoms are thus oblique to the plane of the paper. (b) Projection of lattice on plane containing the C-axis and the dotted line in (a). The atoms shown are in four different planes (12), (345,) (678), (90).

cubically. Studies of ordinary ice by X-ray diffraction have shown that the molecules, or rather, the oxygen atoms are arranged in layers of hexagonal rings. The atoms in a ring are not in one plane but in two however: alternate atoms are in the upper and lower planes. The spacing between these two planes is much less than the spacing between the layers. Adjacent layers are mirror images of each other. Figure 2.3 shows this arrangement and its relation to the tetrahedral structure. The structure of the ice crystal resembles that of a hexagonal metal such as magnesium or cadmium. The plane of a layer of hexagonal rings is called the *basal plane* of the crystal. The direction at right angles to the basal plane is the *optic axis* or *C-axis*.

Deformation of a Single Ice Crystal

The way in which an ice crystal deforms under an applied stress has been studied extensively in the laboratory. Glen (1958a, 1963a) has reviewed this work. The deformation of an ice crystal appears to be similar in many ways to that of single crystals of metals. Two important features are that even very low stresses cause some deformation and that the deformation takes place in discrete bands. These bands, which are parallel to the basal plane of the ice crystal, can be seen clearly in polarized light. A single ice crystal normally deforms by gliding on the basal plane, and for a long time this was believed to be the only form of deformation. However, Muguruma and others (1966) have recently observed deformations in crystals oriented for non-basal glide. To produce a given strain, the stress must be about 20 times greater than for basal glide, and the stress–strain curve has a different shape.

The deformation of ice, and of metals, can be understood in terms of the movement of *dislocations* within the crystals (Weertman and Weertman, 1964). Dislocations are irregularities in the crystal structure that allow planes of atoms to move over each other much more easily than they would in a perfect crystal. This explains how even a low stress produces some deformation. Dislocations form because crystal growth is usually somewhat irregular. In addition, the deformation process creates new dislocations. Deformation involves the movement of dislocations within the crystal and the dislocations interact with each other. One dislocation may block the movement of others and so cause them to "pile up" at some points. Dislocations may also pile up at places where the crystal contains an impurity. The interaction of dislocations can explain the process of *work hardening* that is, strengthening a crystalline substance by deforming it. The deformation produces dislocations and these tend to pile up at the boundaries of the planes along which slip is occurring. The piled up dislocations tend to resist further deformation. To soften the material again, the dislocations have to be dispersed into some more nearly uniform arrangement; the dislocations have to move out of their slip planes. Such a movement is called *dislocation climb*.

Webb and Hayes (1967) have observed dislocations in ice by means of an X-ray diffraction technique. They concluded that "The dislocation configurations observed in ice are remarkably similar to those observed in other plastically deformable materials."

When a constant shear stress is applied to an ice crystal the rate of deformation at first increases with time. The ice crystal thus exhibits work softening in contrast to the work hardening observed in metals. However, the deformation rate eventually reaches a steady value if the shear stress remains constant. This type of deformation behaviour is called *creep*. The steady value of strain rate is found to be proportional to a power n of the shear stress. Here shear stress and strain rate refer to the values across the basal plane of the crystal. Different experimenters have obtained values of n in the range 1·5 to 3·9 with a mean of about 2·5. The factor of proportionality, but not the value of n, depends on the temperature. The lower the temperature, the smaller the strain rate produced by a given shear stress.

Weertman (1955, 1957c, 1957d) has considered several models which might explain crystal deformation in terms of dislocations. These lead to power law relations between strain rate and stress. The index in the power law varies according to which particular dislocation mechanism is assumed to control the deformation rate. These models also predict that strain rate is related to temperature according to Boltzmann's law; this agrees with observation. Only two of the proposed models could apply to ice. In one of these, the rate of dislocation climb controls the deformation rate and this leads to a power law with $n = 4.5$. The other model gives $n = 3$ (Weertman, 1963). The experimental data cannot be used to decide which model is the more appropriate; the spread of experimental values of n is too great. Nevertheless, the overall agreement suggests that dislocation theory can provide a satisfactory explanation of the main features of the deformation of ice crystals.

One of the apparent discrepancies between the behaviour of ice and that of metals is in the matter of glide direction. We have seen that an ice crystal deforms by gliding in the basal plane. In metals, gliding usually occurs more readily in some direction than in others in this plane. In this case one observes differences between the glide direction and the direction of the applied shear stress. With ice, such experiments have usually yielded negative results. Kamb (1961) has suggested an explanation. He showed that, for hexagonal crystals in which strain rate is related to shear stress by a power law with n between 1 and 5, any difference between the glide direction and the direction of the shear stress will never be more than a few degrees. Such a difference is too small to be detected experimentally. Kamb's argument rests on the assumptions that gliding occurs simultaneously in three symmetry-equivalent directions in the glide plane and that, in each of these directions, strain rate and shear stress components are related by the power law. However, Glen and Jones (1968) have recently observed a definite difference between the glide direction and the direction of the shear stress, in ice at $-50°C$. The assumption of simultaneous glide in the three directions appears to be incorrect: once gliding starts in one direction it appears to "run away with itself". This happens in some other substances such as NaCl.

Polycrystalline Ice

The deformation of polycrystalline aggregates of ice has also been studied in the laboratory (Glen, 1958a, 1963a). The usual method is to apply uniaxial compression or tension or simple shear and measure the deformation, under constant stress, as a function of time. In contrast to the case of single crystals, the strain rate for polycrystals initially decreases with time. Thereafter the strain rate reaches a steady value. However, at higher stresses, the strain rate may eventually start to increase again and finally attain another steady value. The initial stage of decreasing strain rate is referred to as *primary* or *transient creep*. This stage is not of much interest in glacier studies because stresses in glaciers act for long periods. The two stages of constant strain rate are called *secondary* or *quasi-viscous creep* and *tertiary creep*.

In both secondary and tertiary stages, the strain rate is found to be proportional to a power of the stress. Measured values of the index n are in the range 1·9 to 4·5 with a mean of about 3. It is also found that, for randomly oriented polycrystals in simple shear, the strain rate for a given shear stress is only about one hundredth of the strain rate which the same shear stress would produce in a single crystal, if it were applied across the basal plane.

Several processes contribute to the deformation of polycrystalline ice. In addition to the sliding of individual crystals on their basal planes, crystals may move relative to each other. Crystal growth, the migration of crystal boundaries, and recrystallization are also important (Shumskiy, 1958; Gold, 1963). The relative importance of these mechanisms, which depends on the amount of deformation and on the applied stress, has not yet been clearly established. However, the observation that a given shear stress produces a much smaller strain rate in polycrystals than in a single crystal can be attributed to the fact that few crystals in a polycrystalline aggregate will be oriented for glide in the direction of the applied stress. The initial decrease in strain rate after application of a stress may be due to interference between crystals with different orientations. The final increase in strain rate results from the production, by recrystallization, of crystals oriented for glide in the direction of the applied shear stress.

Steinemann (1954, 1958a) has studied the changes in crystal size and orientation produced by stress. He subjected bars of ice to tensions or compressions in the range 0·7 to 16 kg cm^{-2}. (Shear stresses in glaciers seldom exceed 1·5 kg cm^{-2}.) He also compressed thin sections of ice between rubber sheets, at stresses between 4 and 44 kg cm^{-2}. The temperature of the ice was $-4·8°C$. The ice grains were randomly oriented at the start of the experiments, and most had simple shapes. (A "grain" of ice is a single crystal, but a grain of snow may consist of several crystals.)

Steinemann found that recrystallization occurred when the deformation exceeded a few per cent. There were two types of recrystallization: recrystallization during stress and recrystallization after the stress was removed. These had different results. Recrystallization under stress produced a system of complex interlocking grains. The size of the grains depended on the stress: the higher the stress the smaller the grains. Moreover the grains were no longer randomly oriented, but showed a preferred orientation with their basal planes in the direction of the applied shear stress. (A uniaxial stress is equivalent to a shear stress across a plane at 45° to the direction of the uniaxial stress.) Recrystallization after the stress was removed resulted in a considerable increase in grain size. Moreover, the grains no longer interlocked, although their shapes remained complex.

Steinemann also found that the more impurities there were in the ice the more readily it recrystallized. Impurities in metals have the opposite effect.

Rigsby (1960) has made somewhat similar observations. He deformed polycrystals by shear stresses in the range 3·5 to 5 kg cm^{-2}. The temperature was $-2°C$. One specimen, consisting of 16 small blocks of ice frozen together, was deformed for about 2 months. During this time the original 16 blocks recrystallized into some 135 grains and there was considerable migration of grain boundaries. The specimen was then held at a temperature of $-0·3°C$ for 3 days: many changes in grain boundaries were observed. Rigsby also deformed fine-grained ice in which, initially, the C-axes were randomly oriented. After deformation, the sample showed a preferred orientation with the C-axis perpendicular to the direction of shear.

Rigsby also found that the ice recrystallized after the applied stress was removed. Recrystallization was rapid at temperatures near the melting point but seemed "almost to have stopped" at temperatures below $-10°C$. In bent crystals, recrystallization was most rapid at the sharpest part of the bend. In one experiment, Rigsby took a sample of ice from a tunnel at the edge of the Greenland ice sheet, where the temperature was well below the melting point, and kept it just below $0°C$ for about a month. The sample originally consisted of over 300 crystals with a strongly preferred orientation. The "annealing" process reduced the sample to sixteen large crystals. The directions of the C-axes of these sixteen crystals had a much larger spread than that found in the original crystals.

Measurement of Size and Orientation of Ice Crystals

As measurement of crystal size and orientation is an important technique in glacier studies, we shall describe it briefly. A report by Langway (1958) gives further details.

The method makes use of the optical properties of an ice crystal. A ray of light incident parallel to the C-axis is transmitted normally. A ray incident in any other direction is split into two rays, which travel through the crystal with different velocities and so are refracted by different amounts. This property is called *birefringence*. Consider an ice crystal placed between crossed polaroids with its C-axis in the direction of transmission of the light. The plane polarized light beam emerging from the first polaroid screen will be transmitted unchanged by the ice crystal. The beam will not be transmitted by the second polaroid screen as its plane of polarization is at right angles to that of the first. Such a crystal will appear dark. Crystals oriented in other directions will modify the plane polarized beam however and some light will then be transmitted by the second polaroid. How much depends on the orientation of the crystal.

Between the crossed polaroids a section of ice, generally about

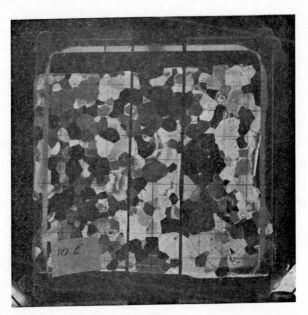

Fig. 2.4. Thin section of ice photographed in polarized light. The grid is 1 cm. The two dark lines are bands holding the sample in place.

1 mm thick

which can

ual crystals

ent among

is an example

mine often

appears dark

transmitted

fied. One of

of light, (Fig

(Fig 2.50)

an equator

1 mm thick, is placed on a "universal stage". This is a mount which can be rotated about horizontal and vertical axes. Individual crystals can be distinguished because each transmits a different amount of light according to its orientation. Figure 2.4 is an example. The size of each crystal can be measured. To determine orientation the mount is rotated until a particular crystal appears dark. Its C-axis is then parallel to the direction of the transmitted light. (The above description is slightly oversimplified. One or two other orientations may also result in extinction of light.) Crystal orientations are plotted on a "Schmidt diagram" (Fig. 2.5a). This represents the inner surface of a hemisphere on an equal-area projection. Each dot represents the intersection

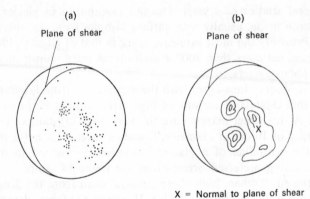

X = Normal to plane of shear

Fig. 2.5. Schmidt Diagram. Each point in (a) represents the intersection of the C-axis of one crystal with the surface of a hemisphere. The contours in (b) represent 1, 3, 5 per cent of points per 1 per cent of area.

of the C-axis of one crystal with the surface of the hemisphere. If the pattern is not random, contours of the percentage of points per 1 per cent of area can be drawn (Fig. 2.5b). This is known as a "fabric diagram". Figure 2.5 illustrates a fabric with not one but four preferred orientations, a type that will be mentioned again later.

Glacier Ice

We now discuss how observations of ice crystals in glaciers compare with the laboratory results.

The ice in an active glacier is a mass of interlocking, roughly equigranular crystals. Relative movement between crystals is limited, but each crystal may deform internally. However, the fact that the general shape of the crystals does not change greatly with time shows that deformation is accompanied by recrystallization. Initially, the ice crystals must be randomly oriented because this is the case for the firn grains from which they are derived. However, a preferred orientation can develop by recrystallization.

Several studies of crystal size and orientation in glacier ice have been made, usually with surface samples from the ablation area. Probably the most extensive work is that of Rigsby (1960). He examined more than 8000 samples from three temperate and three polar glaciers.

Most observations agree with the expectation from laboratory work that crystals in regions of high stress should be relatively small. At the other extreme are the very large crystals, often of the order of 10 cm in diameter, found in stagnant ice. Ice from near the centreline of a glacier is randomly oriented in most cases. Strong preferred orientations are found in samples from near the edge, where high shear stresses result from the drag of the valley walls on the moving ice. However, the fabric diagrams usually have three or four maxima, instead of a single one in the direction perpendicular to the plane of shear. Figure 2.5 shows a typical four maximum or "diamond" pattern. The normal to the plane of shear is usually near the centre of the diamond.

Observations at depth are scanty. Kamb and Shreve (1963) have drilled right through Blue Glacier, U.S.A. and obtained cores from various depths. Crystal size increased slightly down to 70 m and then decreased to the bottom at 137 m. The fabric diagrams varied with depth, but below 100 m they had three or four maxima. Gow (1963a) has studied cores from the Ross Ice Shelf in Antarctica. He found that the crystal size increased with depth. Below 65 m, the fabric diagrams had three or four maxima and these became more pronounced with increasing depth. (The thickness of ice at the drill hole was 258 m.) It was uncertain what stresses were acting in this part of the ice shelf. On the other hand, Rigsby (1960) found a fabric with a single strong maximum in ice from a tunnel at the edge of the Greenland ice sheet.

Patterns with three or four maxima have never been obtained in the laboratory, either by applying stress or after its removal. There is at present no explanation of why they are found in glaciers. Two plausible ideas can be excluded. As the patterns occur near the glacier bed, where stresses are large, they cannot have been produced by recrystallization after the reduction of stress. The fact that they appear in both temperate and cold glaciers eliminates the possibility of some temperature-dependent effect.

Changes to glacier ice, more conspicuous than these modifications to individual crystals, also occur during flow. One of these is the development of *foliation*. This is a structure consisting of a series of alternate plane layers of clear and bubbly ice, or sometimes alternate layers of fine-grained and coarse ice. Each layer may be only a few centimetres wide, but the pattern is repeated many times. Foliation is probably produced in regions of exceptionally high stress such as the base of an icefall; but the precise mechanism is obscure.

Allen and others (1960) have described foliation visible throughout the ablation area of Blue Glacier. On the surface, the foliation forms a pattern of concentric arcs, convex down glacier. The pattern in three dimensions has been described as a series of "nested spoons". Blue Glacier has a large icefall not far above the equilibrium line. Allen and others suggested that the foliation originates in the icefall as vertical planes transverse to the direction of flow. The planes are then gradually transformed to "nested spoons" by differential movement as the ice moves faster near the centreline than at the sides and faster on the surface than at depth.

The processes leading to the fabric, foliation, and other structures observed in glacier ice are not well understood at present. Much work remains to be done.

CHAPTER 3

THE MASS BALANCE OF A GLACIER

"Wavering between the profit and the loss."
T. S. ELIOT, *Ash Wednesday*.

Introduction

Mass balance studies are concerned with changes in the mass of a glacier and the distribution of these changes in space and time. More particularly, to measure the change in mass in a given year. Such studies form an important link in the chain of events connecting advances and retreats of glaciers with changes in climate. Variations in climatic parameters cause variations in the amount of snow which collects on the glacier and in the amount of snow and ice lost by melting. Such changes in mass initiate a complex series of changes in the flow of the glacier which ultimately results in a change in the position of the terminus. The present chapter deals only with measurement of changes in mass. Correlation of these changes with meteorological data, and the response of the glacier to the changes, will be discussed separately.

Measurements of this kind may have considerable practical importance. In several countries glacier-fed streams supply much of the water used by hydroelectric plants. Such streams have a distinctive pattern of run-off. A glacier acts as a natural reservoir which stores water during the winter and releases it in summer. Especially large quantities may be released in warm summers when water from other sources is in short supply. Mass balance measurements determine how much water can be stored and released in this way, and what variations can be expected from year to year.

In this subject in the past, different authors have used the same terms with different meanings. Much confusion has resulted. We shall therefore start with some definitions. Methods of measurement will then be described and some typical results given. Finally we shall discuss the special problem of determining the mass balance of the Antarctic ice sheet.

Definitions

The definitions given here are the most recent proposals of Meier (1967). Ideally, definitions should be applicable to glaciers and ice sheets of all sizes and types. Definitions must be comprehensible as well as comprehensive, however, and these two requirements may sometimes conflict. The following should cover the great majority of practical cases.

The income and expenditure terms in the glacier's budget are represented by accumulation and ablation. Accumulation includes all processes by which material is added to the glacier. Material is normally added as snow which is slowly transformed to ice. Avalanches, rime formation, and formation of ice by refreezing of meltwater are some other accumulation processes. Accumulation normally takes place at or near the glacier surface. Ablation includes all processes by which snow and ice are lost from the glacier. Melting followed by run-off, evaporation, removal of snow by wind, the calving of icebergs are examples. Melting followed by refreezing at another part of the glacier is not ablation because the glacier does not lose mass. Practically all the ablation takes place at the surface or, in the case of calving, at the terminus. Some glaciers may lose ice by melting at their bases, but the amount lost is negligible compared with surface ablation.

In mass balance studies, thicknesses of snow and ice are measured vertically rather than perpendicular to the surface. Mass balance measurements at points are normally expressed as equivalent volumes of water per unit area: thus they have the dimension of length. Measurements are usually made at points which move with the ice (a stake set in the ice for example). Such observations may have to be corrected to fixed points before volume changes, or averages over areas, are computed.

If we were to make repeated measurements of the thickness of a glacier at a given point, we would find that it varied during the year. The thickness would probably attain a maximum in late spring or early summer and a minimum in late summer. In most glaciers we can identify, at a later date, the surface formed at the time of minimum thickness. It may be marked by a layer of dirt for example. This surface is called the *summer surface*. If t_1, t_2 are the times of two successive minima, and t_m the time of the intervening maximum, the interval t_1 to t_2 is called the *balance year*. The length of the balance year will not be exactly 365 days and it will vary slightly from year to year. However, its average length should be close to 365 days. (This statement may not hold in low latitudes. Glaciers in Africa have two balance years in each calendar year.) The balance year can be divided into a *winter season* (t_1 to t_m) and a *summer season* (t_m to t_2). At the end of the summer, snow may be accumulating on the higher parts of a glacier while ablation continues near the terminus. Thus the length of the balance year, and of the summer and winter seasons, may vary from place to place on the glacier.

We now define the basic quantities. At a given point on a glacier at a given time, the *accumulation rate $\dot{c}$* is the rate of increase of water-equivalent thickness. Similarly the *ablation rate $\dot{a}$* is the rate of decrease of thickness. In practice we measure time integrals of these quantities, starting at t_1. These integrals (from t_1 to an arbitrary time t) are called *accumulation c* and *ablation a*. The integrals from t_1 to t_2 are the *total accumulation c_t* and *total ablation a_t*. Total accumulation can be expressed as the sum of *winter accumulation c_w* and *summer accumulation c_s*. Total ablation can be similarly subdivided. Accumulation is always taken to be positive, ablation negative.

The *balance* or *mass balance b* at any time is the algebraic sum of the accumulation and ablation. It is the change in mass (expressed as equivalent volume of water) per unit area relative to the previous summer surface. The mass balance at the end of the balance year is the *net balance b_n* for the year. It can be subdivided into a *winter balance* b_w, which is positive, and a *summer balance* b_s, which is negative.

Thus

$$b = c + a = \int_{t_1}^{t} (\dot{c} + \dot{a})\, dt$$

$$b_n = b_w + b_s = c_t + a_t$$

$$= c_w + a_w + c_s + a_s = \int_{t_1}^{t_m} (\dot{c} + \dot{a})\, dt + \int_{t_m}^{t_2} (\dot{c} + \dot{a})\, dt$$

The glacier can be divided into an *accumulation area* where $b_n > 0$ and an *ablation area* where $b_n < 0$. The boundary between the two areas is the *equilibrium line*.

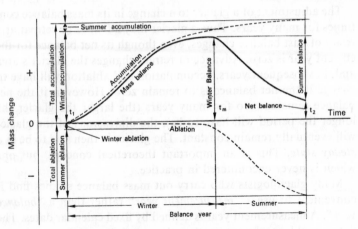

FIG. 3.1. Definitions of mass balance terms.

Figure 3.1 shows the different quantities and how they vary during the year. This diagram refers to a point in the accumulation area.

Mass balance quantities, analogous to those defined for a point, can be defined for an area. They have the dimensions of volume. Such quantities are denoted by capital letters. One can also obtain mean values by averaging over an area, usually the whole area of the glacier.

The *average net balance* $\bar{b}_n = B_n/S$, where S is the area of the glacier, is the most useful parameter for summarizing the change in a glacier in a given year. A difficulty arises, at least in theory, in summing values of b_n at individual points to obtain a value B_n for the whole glacier. This is because the balance year, and the summer and winter seasons, are not the same at all points on the glacier. Differences of a few days can be ignored: otherwise the balance year should be taken as the time between two successive minima of the mass of the glacier as a whole. Measurements at individual points are then adjusted to these dates. Another difficulty in computing $\bar{b}_n$ is that the area of the glacier may change during a year. Strictly speaking, area should be defined as the area at the end of the balance year.

The adjustment of a glacier to a change in its mass balance continues for many years. Thus a glacier may advance or retreat as a result of past balance changes, even though its net balance for the current year is zero. Advance or retreat changes the glacier's area and, in subsequent years, accumulation and ablation will have to change if the net balance is to remain zero. However, if the net balance remains zero for many years (the larger the glacier the longer the period will have to be), the dimensions of the glacier will eventually remain constant. The glacier is then said to be in a *steady state*. This is an important theoretical concept, but one which is never encountered in practice.

Many glaciologists who carry out mass balance studies find it convenient to use a "*measurement year*" rather than a "*balance year*". A measurement year is defined by fixed calendar dates. The date should be chosen so that the measurement year starts at about the same time as a balance year. October 1st would be a suitable date in the northern hemisphere.

The previous definitions have to be modified in this fixed date system. In the definitions of accumulation, ablation, and balance, the time integrals now begin on the first day of the measurement year. The integrals of accumulation rate and ablation rate over the whole measurement year are called the *annual accumulation* c_a

and *annual ablation* a_a. The *annual balance* b_a is the algebraic sum of c_a and a_a. Winter and summer seasons are not defined in this system.

The measurement year is unlikely to coincide with the balance year. Thus, in any year, the annual balance will not be the same as the net balance. The average values of these two quantities, taken over many years, should, however, be approximately equal. The values of annual accumulation and total accumulation, also of annual ablation and total ablation, will be related in a similar way.

Direct Measurement of Net Balance

The net balance of a glacier can be determined in more than one way. The usual method is measurement of net balance at a representative set of points on the glacier. The following must be measured:

1. The mass of snow and ice, accumulated during the current balance year, which remains at the end of the year. This is the net balance b_n at points in the accumulation area S_c.

2. The mass of ice lost from the ablation area during the year. This is the net balance b_n at points in the ablation area S_a. The net balance B_n of the glacier is then determined from the relation

$$B_n = \int_{S_c} b_n \, dS + \int_{S_a} b_n \, dS$$

3. In many studies the winter balance is also measured and the summer balance obtained as the difference between the winter balance and the net balance. These quantities are determined because attempts are often made to correlate mass balance measurements with meteorological data. The correlation is usually higher for winter balance and summer balance than it is for net balance.

We shall now outline methods of measuring these quantities. The first and second involve measurements at the end of the balance year: the third, at the end of the winter season. We are concerned only with changes in mass over periods of several months. Obtaining reliable measurements becomes increasingly difficult as the time interval is reduced.

1. Pits have to be dug, or cores taken, to measure net balance in the accumulation area. The previous "summer surface" must of course be located. This surface may be marked by a layer of dirt in the firn, or by a sudden change in density, hardness, or grain size. In arctic glaciers a low-density layer of "depth hoar" often proves useful (see Chapter 2). Depth hoar is formed in autumn by sublimation within the snow cover. The base of the layer of depth hoar is taken as the summer surface. In continuing studies, each summer surface can be marked by dye or strings. Marking is essential if the measurements are referred to fixed dates rather than to the end of the balance year.

One must measure both the thickness and density of the layer between the surface (at the end of the balance year) and the previous summer surface. The density of snow and firn can be determined by weighing a known volume. For ice it may be sufficiently accurate to assume a density of 0.9 g cm^{-3}. When the firn is interspersed with layers and lenses of ice, the proportions of firn and ice must be estimated. A pit is better than a core for this purpose, as the pit provides a much larger sampling area.

In some cases meltwater may percolate through the current year's firn and refreeze in lower layers. If this happens, measurements must not be confined to the top layer. The density of the layer of the previous year, and possibly of earlier years also, must be checked. An alternative technique is to place a tray just below the surface at the end of the balance year. In the following summer, the tray will collect the water which would otherwise penetrate into the layers below. At the end of the summer, the net balance is obtained from the mass of ice (or water) in the tray plus the mass of firn above it.

2. Measurements are simple in the ablation area. Stakes, set in holes drilled in the ice, are used as references. The distance between the top of the stake and the ice surface is measured at the beginning and end of the balance year. The difference between the two is multiplied by 0.9 to convert it to water-equivalent balance.

If a glacier loses a significant amount of ice by calving, the ice velocity and thickness must be measured on a line across the glacier near its terminus. The loss by calving during the year can then be calculated.

3. In the accumulation area, the winter balance is determined in the same way as the net balance, but the measurements are made at the end of the winter season instead of the end of the balance year. In the ablation area, the ice surface can be located by probing through the winter's snow cover. The depth of snow is thus easily measured. A few density measurements have to be made as well. The summer balance can be obtained by subtracting the net balance from the winter balance.

To determine the net balance of the whole glacier, the measurements must be made at a representative set of points. The data are plotted on a map and contours of equal net balance drawn. Supplementary information such as the position of the snow line at different times during the summer, and the detailed topography of the glacier surface, can be of considerable value in drawing these contours. The net balance (B_n) and the average net balance $(\bar{b}_n)$ can then be determined.

A map with contours of elevation and of net balance can be used to determine the average net balance for elevation intervals of say 100 m. A graph of net balance against elevation can then be drawn. This is a useful way to present results. The area of the glacier in each elevation interval and also the net balance of the area (that is, average net balance multiplied by area) in the same intervals can be shown on the same graph. Figure 3.2 is an example. These data, which were obtained by Pytte and Østrem (1965), refer to Nigardsbreen in Norway for the 1963–4 balance year. The average net balance was a gain of 95 cm.

The accuracy of mass balance measurements is difficult to assess. Lack of precision in measuring thickness or density of layers may at times produce appreciable errors. But the main source of inaccuracy lies in the problems of sampling. Measurements can be made only at a limited number of points and many glaciers have large crevassed areas where no measurements are possible. Have enough points been used? How well does each point represent the area around it? And how well does the set of points represent

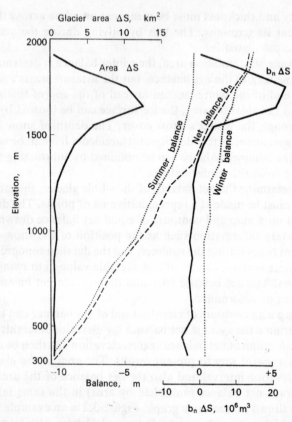

FIG. 3.2. Mass balance data: Nigardsbreen, Norway. From Pytte
and Østrem (1965).

conditions over the glacier as a whole? It is very difficult to answer these questions.

The number of points needed on a particular glacier depends on
the size of the variations in accumulation and ablation from place
to place. As many as 120 points per km² have been used; but one
cannot lay down an absolute figure. Also, what is desirable has
often to be modified to what is practicable. Variations are usually

greater in the accumulation area than elsewhere; a greater density of points should be used there. On most glaciers the patterns of accumulation and ablation show some consistency from year to year, even though values vary widely. Thus, in a continuing study, the number of points can be reduced after a few years, when the measurements have shown which points appear to be typical of wide areas.

The best way to assess the reliability is to determine the mass balance by two or more methods and compare results. Alternatives to the direct method will now be described.

Photogrammetric Method

In this method, an accurate contour map of the glacier is made at intervals of one or a few years. Some form of photogrammetry is the only feasible method. Comparison of two maps determines the change in volume of the glacier in the intervening period. This can be converted to the change in mass by using average densities for firn and ice. One must also assume that, at any point on the glacier, the distribution of density with depth does not change with time. This assumption should be valid in the ablation area. But it may be questionable near the equilibrium line, especially if the position of this line varies appreciably from year to year.

This method only determines the mass balance of the glacier, not the balance at specific points. The vectors of ice movement are not parallel to the glacier surface; there is a small component of flow perpendicular to the surface. This component is downwards relative to the surface in the accumulation area and upwards in the ablation area. Thus flow tends to counteract surface elevation changes produced by accumulation and ablation. (If it didn't, the surface would always be growing steeper.) In addition, compaction of snow and firn changes the surface level in the accumulation area. The change of elevation of a point on the glacier surface, as determined by comparison of two maps, is the net result of all these processes, not the result of accumulation and ablation alone. Thus the photogrammetric method only determines the change in mass of the whole glacier.

Except near the terminus, the annual change in surface level will probably be of the order of a few tens of centimetres. Thus a high standard of contouring accuracy is required. This can be attained with modern plotting equipment.

Timing of the photography is of great importance. If the results are to have any glaciological significance, the map must show the glacier at the end of the balance year. Otherwise any measured volume change may merely reflect the fact that the melt season was more advanced at the time of photography in one year than in the other. If it is essential to take the photographs before the end of the summer, the ablation between the time of photography and the end of the balance year must be measured on the glacier. This has not often been done in such studies in the past.

To determine the net balance for individual years by this method, a map must be made every year. This will probably be impracticable on account of expense, if for no other reason. However, maps made at intervals of a few years can provide a valuable check on results of a detailed mass balance study. Such maps also provide useful data about changes in glaciers where detailed measurements cannot be made. A measurement of the change in mass is a much better indication of a glacier's "state of health" than the advance or retreat of its terminus is.

Hydrologic Method

This method also determines only the net balance of the whole glacier. Measurements must be made over the complete drainage basin in which the glacier lies. Stream gauges are used to measure the total run-off from the basin (R). In addition, the total precipitation over the basin (P) must be measured. Adequate sampling is the main difficulty in this case. The amount of water, ice, and snow lost by evaporation (E) must also be measured or estimated. This term will probably be small compared with the others. If each of these quantities are totals over the balance year and are expressed as volumes of water, the net balance of the glacier (B_n) can be obtained by the equation

$$B_n = P - R - E$$

Tangborn (1966) has compared the net balance of South Cascade Glacier, U.S.A., as determined by the hydrologic method, with the net balance obtained by measurements on the glacier. The two methods gave net balances, averaged over seven years, which were within 5 per cent of each other.

Reconnaissance Methods

As a mass balance study is a major undertaking, detailed measurements can only be made on a few glaciers. For some purposes, a little information about the mass balance of a large number of glaciers in a region may be more valuable than detailed measurements on one or two. Or at least such information may supplement detailed studies. Aerial photographs, or a reconnaissance flight over a glacier, can tell us something about its mass balance. LaChapelle (1962) has discussed this question and Meier and Post (1962) have used the method to study glaciers in western North America. As before, such observations should be made as near the end of the summer as possible.

The equilibrium line can be easily located on glaciers in temperate regions. It coincides roughly with the snow line at the end of the summer. A low snow line which has a sharply-defined boundary with bare ice indicates that the net balance is probably positive. If the boundary is sharp but the snow line high, there has been increased accumulation after several years of negative net balance. A snow line separated from bare ice by an area of old firn indicates that the net balance is more negative than in the preceding few years.

If the boundaries of the accumulation area can be distinguished on a map or aerial photographs, one can calculate the accumulation area ratio (the area of the accumulation area divided by the area of the whole glacier). A rule of thumb, found to hold in quite a few cases, is that an accumulation area ratio of about 0·7 corresponds to a net balance of zero (Glen, 1963b). Alternatively, the elevation of the equilibrium line can be determined. On any given glacier, variations in this elevation from year to year can be used as an indicator of variations in net balance.

On arctic glaciers, the equilibrium line is usually at a lower elevation than the snow line at the end of the summer. Between them lies an area where there is a net accumulation of super-imposed ice (see Chapter 2). There is then no simple method of locating the equilibrium line.

Results

Isolated measurements of accumulation and ablation have been made for a long time. Some of the first measurements of the mass balance of a whole glacier were those of Ahlmann (1935b, 1946). Between 1941 and 1948 Wallen (1948) measured the mass and energy balances of Karsa Glacier in Sweden. Since then several long-term investigations have been started. Those of Schytt (1962) on Stor Glacier in Sweden (started 1946), Hoinkes and Rudolf (1962a, 1962b) on Hintereisferner in Austria (started 1952), and LaChapelle (1965) on Blue Glacier, U.S.A. (started 1957) may be mentioned. The main aim of these studies has been to try to correlate mass balance variations with meteorological parameters. On the other hand, the work of Meier and Tangborn (1965) on South Cascade Glacier, U.S.A. (started 1957) has been directed to the second problem mentioned at the beginning of this chapter, the response of the glacier to changes in its mass balance. All the above glaciers have two features in common: they are small, and the ice is near the pressure melting temperature. (The area of Hintereisferner is about 10 km². None of the others exceeds 5 km².) Thus the mass balance studies of Müller (1962b) on White Glacier in the Canadian Arctic (started 1959) represent a desirable change. White Glacier is classified as cold. Its area is 38 km².

The results of Schytt for Stor Glacier are quoted in Table 3.1 to show what variations can occur from year to year. Only in one year out of sixteen did this glacier have a positive net balance, and in one other year the net balance was zero. Stor Glacier is obviously not in a steady state with the present climate and its volume decreased by 10 per cent during the period.

Such studies provide data for particular glaciers. Are there any results of wider application? More specifically, does the field work point to any simplifying assumptions which are useful in theoretical analyses? Meier and Tangborn (1965) have proposed such a generalization as a result of their work on South Cascade

TABLE 3.1. AVERAGE WINTER, SUMMER, AND NET BALANCES OF STOR GLACIER
(units are cm)
(Data from Schytt, 1962)

Balance year	b_w	$-b_s$	b_n
1945–6	113	226	−113
1946–7	103	310	−207
1947–8	145	145	0
1948–9	223	132	+ 91
1949–50	142	271	−129
1950–1	81	145	− 64
1951–2	87	103	− 16
1952–3	194	274	− 80
1953–4	113	210	− 97
1954–5	161	177	− 16
1955–6	129	177	− 48
1956–7	161	194	− 33
1957–8	145	210	− 65
1958–9	97	197	−100
1959–60	68	226	−158
1960–1	74	187	−113

Glacier. The graph of net balance versus elevation does not have a simple shape and values of net balance vary widely from year to year. However, the pattern of variation of net balance with elevation appears to vary little with time. Meier and Tangborn suggest that the curves for different years can be regarded as parallel and that one curve can be made to coincide with another merely by a displacement parallel to the X-axis (net balance axis). This rule is a good approximation for South Cascade Glacier, based on 7 years' data. On the other hand it doesn't seem to hold very well for Stor Glacier. It should be tested against data from a wide range of glaciers.

This rule has certain implications. If true, it means that, for any given glacier, once the shape of the curve of net balance versus elevation has been determined, only a single point is needed to fix the curve for any particular year. Thus the glacier's net balance, and the average net balance for each elevation interval, could be determined merely by noting the elevation of the equilibrium line. Few glaciologists would assert that this would be more than a rough approximation.

Mass Balance of the Antarctic Ice Sheet

A problem of current interest is the mass balance of the Antarctic ice sheet. There is no ablation in the interior of the continent; ice is only lost at or near the margins. Thus the net balance is estimated by calculating the total accumulation over the interior and the total ablation round the perimeter, and comparing the two. In a feature of this size, fluctuations from year to year are of little significance, even if it were possible to measure them. The important question is whether the net balance has been approximately zero over the last 50 or 100 years.

Measurements of thickness and density of annual layers in firn normally give the net mass balance. (An "annual layer" is the layer between two successive summer surfaces.) However, in areas where, if there is any melting, the water refreezes in the same annual layer, the net balance is equal to the total accumulation. The accumulation also equals the precipitation, if disturbances due to wind are disregarded. The pattern of accumulation on the Antarctic ice sheet is now reasonably well known, largely as a result of measurements made during and since the International Geophysical Year. The average accumulation in a year (expressed as water equivalent) ranges from 5 cm in the central area to about 70 cm in some coastal regions (Kotlyakov, 1961). The average value is about 17 cm (Dolgushin and others, 1962).

Measurement of ablation is the main difficulty in estimating the net balance of Antarctica. Melting at the base of the floating ice shelves, which surround much of the continent, probably makes a significant contribution to the ablation. But it is extremely difficult to measure. The best way to overcome this problem is to consider that the ice sheet ends at the place where the ice starts to float. The discharge of ice across this boundary must therefore be determined by measuring the ice thickness and velocity. This is still difficult, especially on the large fast-moving glaciers, but less so than making measurements at the under-surfaces of the ice shelves. Determining ice discharge also eliminates the need for direct measurements of the amount of ice lost annually by calving of icebergs, the major factor in ablation in Antarctica. In addition, some ice is lost by melting and run-off at elevations below about 500 m. Some ice is also lost by evaporation and some snow is blown into the sea.

The inadequacy of present ablation data is reflected in current estimates of the average net balance. At least ten figures, ranging from $+8$ to -3 cm, have been published in the past few years. The majority have been positive, however (Dolgushin and others, 1962).

Indirect methods do not hold much promise of providing information on the mass balance in the near future. One possibility would be to try and detect changes in surface elevation in the central part of the ice sheet. Any change in elevation is unlikely to exceed 10 cm y $^{-1}$. As control stations on bedrock cannot be obtained in the interior of Antarctica, present photogrammetric techniques are inadequate to detect changes of less than about 5 m. An alternative would be to try and detect changes of ice thickness by seismic, gravity, or other methods. But even under favourable conditions the accuracy of these is of the order of 5 or 10 m. Another difficulty is to ensure that the second set of measurements is made at the same point relative to bedrock as the first. Thus a minimum period of 50 years would be needed to obtain results by these methods. Precise levelling might be more accurate but very little has been attempted so far.

Observations of changes in position of glacier termini, and of changes in level of the ice against nunataks, indicate recent recession in some areas and no change in others. However, the ice sheet is probably still adjusting to mass balance changes which occurred hundreds or even a few thousand years ago. Thus these observations tell nothing about the present balance.

One further relevant observation is that world sea level has risen by about 6 cm during the last 50 years. An increase in ocean temperature plus a reduction in the size of glaciers other than those in Antarctica, might explain most of this. However, such a rise suggests that the present net balance of Antarctica cannot be highly positive.

The consensus of present opinion is that, while the central part of the ice sheet may be thickening slightly, the net balance is not far from zero.

Further Reading

Journal of Glaciology, vol. 4, number 33 (1962), contains several papers on mass balance studies.

Canadian Journal of Earth Sciences, vol. 3, number 6 (1966), is devoted to papers on various aspects of mapping glaciers.

The special problems in determining the mass balance of a large ice sheet are discussed in a report of a sub-committee appointed by the Commission of Snow and Ice, International Union of Geodesy and Geophysics. This report forms an appendix to a report on methods of measuring glacier variations. The original report is given in Publication 58, International Union of Scientific Hydrology, pp. 306–9 (1962). The appendix is published in *Ice*, vol. 14, pp. 19–24 (1964).

CHAPTER 4

ENERGY EXCHANGE AT A GLACIER SURFACE

"And cold and heat, and summer and winter, and day and night shall not cease."

Book of Genesis.

Introduction

In this chapter we consider the physical processes which control the mass balance of a glacier. The ultimate aim in studying these processes is to solve a basic problem: given a set of meteorological conditions, what change will they produce in a particular glacier?

The relation between accumulation or ablation and weather conditions is often examined from a purely statistical aspect. As expected, correlations have been established between accumulation and precipitation, and between ablation and hours of sunshine. Other analyses have shown that annual ablation is correlated with the number of degree-days above 0°C of the air temperature. However, any given amount of ablation can result from several different combinations of weather conditions. A correlation obtained in one area will not necessarily be true in another. Moreover, a correlation is in itself no evidence of cause and effect and it gives no insight into the physical processes at work. One should first try to understand these processes: there will then be a sound basis for the correlations.

The atmosphere above a glacier surface acts on it by supplying or removing mass and heat. Almost all the mass is supplied as snow: this process is relatively simple. We shall be concerned with the heat exchange. The glacier surface can gain or lose heat by several mechanisms: the problem is to determine their relative importance. Their net result, at any given time and place, will be to change the surface temperature if it is below 0°C, or to cause melting if the surface is already at 0°C and is receiving heat. Run-off of melted ice is generally the main factor in ablation.

The basic processes of heat exchange are the same whether the surface is at its melting point or not. Many of the details are different, however, because in one case the temperature of the surface can change while in the other case it is fixed. These two conditions have different effects on the temperature gradients in the air immediately above the surface. The main glaciological interest is in the ablation process. For this reason, the great majority of studies of heat balance at a glacier surface have been made during the summer. The present discussion is restricted to this case. Readers interested in the case when the surface temperature is well below the melting point are referred to a study in the Antarctic by Liljequist (1957).

This subject is really a branch of micrometeorology. An important part of the work is based on the dynamics of turbulent fluids. This theory is difficult and many problems are still unsolved. The experimental side also presents great difficulties. The first studies of heat exchange at a glacier surface were made by Sverdrup (1935b) in Spitsbergen. These set the pattern for subsequent work: later changes have mainly consisted of refinements in instrumentation.

To study the heat exchange between glacier and atmosphere, we must consider what is happening at the interface between the two, the glacier surface. Restriction of the present discussion to this does not imply that related processes below the surface are not important from other aspects. For example, meltwater will penetrate into the snow. If the temperature at depth is below 0°C, the water will refreeze there and the latent heat released will warm the surrounding snow. This process, taking place in the accumulation areas of many glaciers, is the main factor which produces a "temperate" glacier (see Chapter 10).

We shall first list the different terms in the energy exchange, then explain each term and how it can be measured. Finally we shall discuss the results.

Terms in Energy Exchange

Heat is supplied to the snow or ice surface by:

1. Solar (short-wave) radiation.
2. Long-wave radiation from water vapour and carbon dioxide in the atmosphere.
3. Molecular conduction from the air, if the air temperature increases with height above the surface.
4. Eddy conduction from the air, if the air temperature increases with height above the surface and the air is turbulent.
5. Condensation, on the surface, of water vapour from the air, if the water vapour pressure increases with height. Turbulence will increase the supply of water vapour.
6. Conduction from the underlying ice, if the ice temperature increases with distance below the surface.
7. Freezing of rain.

Heat is lost from the surface by outgoing long-wave radiation and by terms (3) to (6) if the gradients are in the opposite direction to those stated above. Term (3) is very small compared with most of the others and will not be considered further. In practice, measurements of eddy conduction will include molecular conduction as well.

It is convenient to carry out the subsequent discussion in terms of energy flux, i.e. energy per unit area per unit time. The unit 1 cal cm $^{-2}$ is often called 1 langley.

Radiation

The amount of energy falling at normal incidence outside the earth's atmosphere, at the mean distance of the earth from the sun, is called the *solar constant*. Its value is 2·00 cal cm^{-2} min^{-1}. The earth's surface always receives less than this because energy is absorbed and scattered in the atmosphere. For example, from May to the end of July, a horizontal surface at latitude 60°N receives about 1 cal cm^{-2} min^{-1} for a few hours around mid-day, if the sky is clear.

When solar radiation falls on a snow or ice surface, a certain amount is reflected there. The remainder enters the snow where scattering, reflection and absorption occur. These processes depend to some extent on the wavelength of the radiation, as is demonstrated by the fact that visible light, as it penetrates snow, rapidly becomes blue.

Reflective properties are expressed in terms of the *albedo* of the surface. An albedo of α implies that a fraction $1-\alpha$ of the incident radiation is absorbed. The albedo of any surface is not strictly constant. It varies with elevation of the sun and amount of cloud, for instance. Typical values of albedo for short-wave radiation are about 0·7 to 0·9 for fresh snow, 0·4 to 0·6 for firn, and 0·2 to 0·4 for glacier ice. Thus a glacier surface at the time and place specified in the previous example would absorb about 48 cal cm^{-2} hr^{-1} if the surface were dirty ice, but only about 12 cal cm^{-2} hr^{-1} if the surface were covered by fresh snow.

The earth's surface also receives long-wave radiation from water vapour and carbon dioxide in the atmosphere. This occurs under clear skies as well as cloudy conditions, although the amounts of radiation vary. The radiation under clear skies depends on the air temperature. Typical values are about 14 cal cm^{-2} hr^{-1} and 23 cal cm^{-2} hr^{-1} for free air temperatures of $-10°C$ and $+10°C$ respectively. Long-wave radiation from a cloud cover is approximately equal to that from a black body at the temperature of the base of the cloud (T_c °K). Thus it is σT_c^4, where σ, Stefan's constant, has the value $4·92 \times 10^{-9}$ cal cm^{-2} hr^{-1} deg^{-4}.

The albedo of a snow or ice surface for long-wave radiation is virtually zero; all the incident radiation is absorbed. However, such a surface also emits radiation as a black body at the temperature of the surface. From the preceding formula we deduce that a melting snow or ice surface radiates about 27 cal cm^{-2} hr^{-1}.

As an example, consider a horizontal snow surface (albedo 0·8), in latitude 60°, at mid-day in fine weather in summer. If the air temperature is 0° C, the surface gains about 12 cal cm^{-2} hr^{-1} of short-wave and 18 cal cm^{-2} hr^{-1} of long-wave radiation. Thus 3 cal cm^{-2} hr^{-1} is available for melting. This will produce about 0·4 mm of water per hour. If the air temperature drops to $-6°C$ the incoming long-wave radiation is reduced to 15 cal

cm^{-2} hr^{-1}, and the surface is in equilibrium as far as radiation is concerned.

In the case of a complete heavy overcast, the net energy gained by the surface is simply $\sigma (T_c^4 - T_s^4)$, where T_c, T_s are temperatures of cloud and surface respectively. Long-wave radiation from clouds at 5°C will melt about 0·25 mm of ice per hour. Whenever the temperature of the cloud base is above 0°C the surface gains heat from the atmosphere. This may happen quite frequently in summer on glaciers in temperate regions.

These examples are merely illustrations. In practice cloud temperatures will seldom be known. Also, calculation is difficult for the case of partly cloudy conditions. The usual procedure is to measure net short-wave and net total radiation by radiometers. Net long-wave radiation can be determined by subtraction. There are various sources of error. The response of some types of radiometer depends on the angle of incidence of the radiation; the corrections for this may be uncertain. Thus measurements made when the sun is low may be unreliable. Radiation reflected from an instrument may affect the surface underneath it. Great difficulties are experienced in obtaining readings in periods of snow, rain, or fog, or when rime is being deposited. Thus to obtain radiation measurements typical of all weather conditions is practically impossible.

Radiation is usually the dominating factor in the energy balance, but it is by no means the only one. Other factors will now be discussed.

Energy Transfer by Turbulence

In this section we shall consider the convection of heat and water vapour in the air in the first 2 or 3 m above the surface. Transfer of water vapour results in condensation or evaporation at the surface and thus in liberation or absorption of latent heat. Condensation of 1 g of water vapour on a surface liberates enough heat to melt about 7·5 g of ice. The obvious way to evaluate these terms would be to measure directly the vertical fluxes of heat and water vapour in the air. Instrumental difficulties have prevented anyone from doing this so far. Indirect methods have to be used. These involve measurements of the variations of temperature and vapour pressure with height above the surface. The wind is of course a vital factor in convection, and the variations of wind speed with height have to be measured as well.

The vertical flux of heat due to molecular conduction in the air is

$$\varphi = -K \, \partial T/\partial y = -k\varrho c_p \, \partial T/\partial y \qquad (1)$$

Here, K is thermal conductivity, k is thermal diffusivity, ϱ is density, c_p is specific heat at constant pressure, T is temperature, and y is height above the surface measured positive upwards. The transfer of heat by convection is regarded as analogous to conduction, with eddies playing the part of molecules. The vertical flux of heat due to convection is therefore written as

$$\varphi_h = -A_h \, \varrho c_p \, \partial T/\partial y \qquad (2)$$

Here A_h is called the *coefficient of eddy diffusivity*. In the atmosphere, molecular conduction is insignificant compared with convection and $A_h \approx 10^5 \, k$. In general, A_h is a function of y. If its value is known, φ_h can be calculated by measurements of T at different heights. As the surface temperature is fixed, $\partial T/\partial y$ and therefore φ_h, will be the greater the higher the air temperature is above 0°C.

The vertical flux of water vapour can be treated in a similar way. Analogously to the amount of heat $\varrho c_p T$ per unit volume we have the mass m of water vapour per unit volume. The vertical flux of water vapour can be written

$$\varphi_e = -A_e \, \partial m/\partial y$$

Here A_e is called the *coefficient of eddy diffusion of water vapour*. If e is the pressure of the water vapour in the atmosphere,

$$eM_\omega/m = RT$$

where M_ω is the molecular weight of water and R is the gas constant. But, if P is the atmospheric pressure, M_a the molecular weight of air, and ϱ its density,

$$PM_a/\varrho = RT$$

It follows that

$$m = \varrho e M_\omega / PM_a = 0{\cdot}623 \, \varrho e / P$$

and so

$$\varphi_e = -A_e \, (0{\cdot}623 \, \varrho / P) \, \partial e / \partial y \tag{3}$$

If the surface temperature is 0°C, the pressure of water vapour there will be 4·58 mm Hg. If the vapour pressure in the air above the surface is less than this, ice will be evaporated from the surface. Conversely, if the vapour pressure gradient is positive, water vapour will condense at the surface, which will gain heat as a result. The heat gained by the surface is $-L\varphi_e$, where L is the latent heat. If the value of A_e is known, the flux of water vapour can be determined from equation (3) with measurements of vapour pressure at different heights. In general, air temperatures above 0°C favour condensation, those below 0°C evaporation.

The transfer of heat and water vapour by convection depends on the turbulence of the air. This is measured by the *coefficient of eddy viscosity* A_m given by the equation

$$\tau = A_m \, \varrho \, \partial u / \partial y \tag{4}$$

Here τ is the shear stress in the air above the surface and u is the wind speed at height y above the surface. Equation (4) is equivalent to the flow law of a fluid of kinematic viscosity A_m. This equation is similar to the two preceding ones because shear stress can be regarded as a vertical flux of horizontal momentum.

There is some evidence that, at any given height, the three coefficients A_m, A_h and A_e are approximately equal in an atmosphere which is approximately neutral. (A neutral atmosphere is one in which the temperature gradient is equal to the dry adiabatic lapse rate, $-0{\cdot}986 \times 10^{-2}$ deg m^{-1}.) This assumption is made. The value of the coefficients is determined by calculation of A_m from measurements of wind speed: the method will now be outlined.

The assumption is made that the shear stress τ does not vary with height above the surface. Both theoretical and experimental results suggest that this is a plausible assumption, at least in the first few metres above the surface. Equation (4) then shows that

$$A_m \, \partial u/\partial y = \tau/\varrho = \text{constant}. \tag{5}$$

The quantity $(\tau/\varrho)^{1/2}$ has the dimensions of velocity. It is called the *friction velocity*, denoted u_0.

Measurements have shown that, in atmospheres which are near neutral, the wind speed u above the surface varies as the logarithm of the height. This holds at least in the first 2 m above the surface. The law is written

$$u/u_0 = k_0^{-1} \log y/y_0 \tag{6}$$

Here u_0 is the friction velocity, defined above, k_0 is a dimensionless constant, von Karman's constant, and y_0 is the "*surface roughness parameter*" that is, the height above the surface at which the velocity is zero.

From (5) and (6)

$$A_m = u_0 k_0 y \tag{7}$$

The procedure is to measure wind speed at several heights up to about 3 m. If the relation between u and y is found to be approximately logarithmic, this method can be used. If u_1 and u_2 are the velocities measured at heights y_1 and y_2, the value of y_0 is found from a relation derived from equation (6), namely

$$\log y_0 = (u_1 \log y_2 - u_2 \log y_1)(u_1 - u_2)^{-1}$$

Equations (6) and (7) give

$$A_m = k_0^2 u y (\log y/y_0)^{-1}$$

The value of A_m at different heights is calculated from this relation. Here u is the velocity measured at height y. The value of k_0 is 0·4.

Temperature and vapour pressure are also measured at several heights. The fluxes of heat and water vapour can then be calculated from equations (2) and (3), under the assumption that at each height the values of the coefficients A_m, A_h and A_e are equal. (This assumption is only plausible if wind speed, temperature and vapour pressure all vary as the logarithm of the height.) The fluxes required are those at the surface: they are determined by extrapolation.

Wind speed, temperature and vapour pressure are measured by instruments mounted at different levels on a mast 3 or 4 m high. Thermocouples or thermistors are arranged in pairs with one member of each pair arranged as a wet bulb thermometer. The small size of thermocouples and thermistors minimizes the chance that they will affect the temperature to be measured. They must of course be shielded from radiation. Small electric fans can be used to draw air over the instruments. Wet bulb thermometers are unsatisfactory in very low temperatures: some instrument which measures the dew point should be used in this case. Wind speeds can be measured by small anemometers.

The above method of calculating the fluxes is appropriate in an atmosphere which is neutral or nearly neutral. The atmosphere immediately above a glacier surface is often far from neutral. An increase of temperature of 10 or 15 deg in the first 2 m above the surface has been measured in some cases. With a strong temperature inversion such as this, the atmosphere will be extremely stable. Under stable conditions, wind speed, temperature and vapour pressure may vary with height according to a power law rather than a logarithmic law. Various methods, more or less empirical, have been used to calculate the fluxes in cases where some of the assumptions outlined above do not hold.

Grainger and Lister (1966) have reviewed different laws of wind speed variation with height and compared them with field observations. They consider that the logarithmic law is best not only for neutral but also for extremely stable atmospheres. A power law may be used for moderately stable atmospheres. They conclude that the logarithmic law, with the assumption that the three coefficients have the same value, "may be considered the most applicable for observations in the lowest 2 m above a melting ice surface".

If all else fails, the sum of the fluxes of heat and water vapour can be obtained as the residual term in the equation of conservation of energy. If in unit time the surface receives a net amount of heat H from all sources other than the turbulent transfer of heat and water vapour, if M is the mass of ice melted in unit time, and l is the latent heat of fusion, then

$$\varphi_h + L\varphi_e = lM - H$$

Heat Conduction from Underlying Ice

The heat flux in this case is $-K \, \partial T/\partial y$ where the thermal conductivity and the temperature gradient now refer to the snow or ice. The surface will gain or lose heat according as the temperature increases or decreases with depth. In the early part of the summer the surface will be warmer than the layers immediately below it and heat will be conducted away from the surface. Heat conduction will fall to zero once the whole snow cover has reached the melting temperature. (In fact, heat will flow downwards as a result of the pressure melting gradient. But as this gradient is only about 0·7 deg per 1000 m the heat flow is negligible.) The temperature gradient can be measured by thermocouples or thermistors set at various depths in the snow or ice.

Rain

The heat supplied by rain to each square centimetre of surface per second is $c_w p \, (T_r - T_s)$ where c_w is the specific heat of water, p is the rate of precipitation in g cm $^{-2}$ sec $^{-1}$, and T_r and T_s are the temperatures of the rain and the surface. If the surface is at melting point, rain only transfers a small amount of heat: about 10 cm of rain would have to fall in a day to produce the same amount of heat as does long-wave radiation. (On the assumption that the rain is at the same temperature as the cloud base.) However, if the surface temperature is below freezing point the rain will freeze and each cubic centimetre will release 80 cal to the snow. In this case rain will be a significant source of heat.

Melting

We have reviewed the sources of heat: we now discuss how the heat is used. If the surface receives more heat than it loses, the surplus is used to warm the snow or ice and possibly also for evaporation. After the surface temperature reaches 0°C the surplus heat is used for melting and evaporation. Various studies have shown that evaporation usually constitutes less than 5 per cent of the total ablation. In a few cases the percentage was much higher than this but then the total ablation was small. Thus although evaporation (and condensation) may be significant terms in the energy balance because of the high latent heat, they are of little importance to the mass balance. Melting predominates.

The amount of ice melted over periods of a few days or longer can be measured by ablation stakes. A stake is set in the ice and the change in distance between the ice surface and a fixed mark on the stake is measured. For short-period measurements various type of "ablatograph" have been devised. These consist basically of a float, which remains in contact with the ice surface, and a system of levers to magnify the movement of the float.

Measurement of snow melt is more complicated. LaChapelle (1959a) has discussed this problem. Lowering of the surface, which measures decrease in volume, does not represent the amount of melting because the density of the snow changes with time. The density is measured at different depths and the result has to be corrected for the amount of free water present. Graphs of density against depth at two different times are drawn. The area between the curves represents the total melt over the interval.

The accuracy of the measurements can be checked: the product of the latent heat and the mass of snow and ice melted in unit time must equal the net heat supplied in that time. An alternative approach is to measure all terms except one and obtain the value of that one by subtraction. As mentioned previously, the sum of the two turbulent transfer terms is sometimes obtained in this way. But this approach is less satisfactory.

Relative Importance of Heat Sources

The important heat sources are radiation, convection of heat, and condensation of water vapour. Their relative importance will vary. If the temperature is very low, the amount of water vapour in the atmosphere is very small even though the relative humidity is high. Thus condensation will be appreciable only if both air temperature and humidity are relatively high. There will be little convection if there is no wind. The amount of short-wave radiation depends on the time of year, time of day, and amount of cloud. It is zero at night and during the arctic winter. Variations of surface albedo are also important. The albedo of snow is much higher than that of ice. Thus a glacier surface which does not become free of snow until late July may absorb more solar radiation in August than it absorbs in June, even though the incident radiation is much greater in June.

Measurements made over a limited period of time will reflect the prevailing weather. The best way to obtain figures representative of the whole season might be to measure the relative importance of the terms under several widely different sets of weather conditions. One could then calculate a mean value for the season, weighted according to the frequency of the different conditions. This method would be difficult, however, because some instruments will not work under certain weather conditions. Moreover, the various factors may change in importance over the season, even under similar weather conditions. Table 4.1 illustrates this last point. These data were obtained by Wallen (1948) on Karsa

TABLE 4.1. PERCENTAGES OF TOTAL ABLATION DUE TO DIFFERENT FACTORS
(measurements by Wallen, 1948)

	late May–early June	late July–early August	late August
Radiation	84	45	58
Convection	13	40	32
Condensation	3	15	10

Glacier in Sweden. Radiation provided 84 per cent of the total heat supply in early June but only 45 per cent at the beginning of August. The contribution of condensation increased from 3 to 15 per cent over the same period. The surface was ice in all cases, and each value was obtained by measurements over periods of at least 100 hr.

These facts should be kept in mind in comparing observations from different areas. Results of thirty-two studies are summarized in Table 4·2. These are probably at least three-quarters of all the measurements of this kind made in the ablation season. Table 4·2 shows the amount of heat received from each significant source, expressed as a percentage of the whole. Most authors also analyse the ways in which the heat is expended that is, the percentages used for melting, evaporation and conduction into the ice. These data are not given here.

Different authors present their results in slightly different ways. Some regard net radiation as a heat source. Others treat total absorbed radiation as a source and include outgoing long-wave radiation among the ways in which heat is expended. The latter method of presentation is more informative, but it is not possible when only net radiation is measured. The former method of presentation is adopted here. The column marked "radiation" in Table 4.2 represents net radiation (absorbed short-wave, plus incoming long-wave, minus outgoing long-wave). The "condensation" column represents, in most cases, total heat supplied by condensation; evaporation is regarded separately as a heat sink. In some studies, however, only the net heat (condensation minus evaporation) was measured and in a few others it is not clear whether or not the "condensation" term includes evaporation. These discrepancies should not make much difference to the results, as condensation is usually the smallest of the three sources of heat. Some authors subtract the heat used for evaporation from the absorbed short-wave radiation, but this is not done here. Because the data in Table 4.2 have been reduced to a uniform basis as far as possible, some of the percentages differ slightly from those in previously published summaries.

The different studies give widely different results. Radiation

TABLE 4.2. RELATIVE IMPORTANCE OF HEAT SOURCES IN DIFFERENT AREAS

Location	Position ° '	Surface	Dates	Elev. m	Rad.	Conv.	Cond.	Reference	Note
Ward Hunt Ice Shelf Ellesmere Island	83 12N 74 00W	snow/ ice	60 hr in June, July	15	100			Lister, 1962	1
McGill Ice Cap Axel Heiberg Island	79 41N 90 27W	snow	320 hr in June–Aug.	1530	64	35	1	Havens, 1964	
White Glacier Axel Heiberg Island	79 26N 90 39W	ice	650 hr in July, Aug.	208	48	32	20	Andrews, 1964	
White Glacier Axel Heiberg Island	79 26N 90 39W	ice	20–31 July	208	63	30	7	Havens *et al*, 1965	2
Sveanor snowfield Spitsbergen	79 56N 18 18E	snow	30 June– 6 Aug.	5	24	58	18	Sverdrup, 1935b	
Isachsen's Plateau Spitsbergen	79 09N 12 56E	snow	26 June– 15 Aug.	870	65	23	12	Sverdrup, 1935b	
14th July Glacier Spitsbergen	79 07N 11 55E	snow/ ice	June–Aug.	175	35	65		Sverdrup, 1935b	3, 4
Britannia Glacier N. E. Greenland	77 14N 23 49W	snow/ ice	June, July	620	67	32	1	Lister and Taylor, 1961	
Britannia Glacier N. E. Greenland	77 12N 23 48W	ice	June, July	470	75	20	5	Lister and Taylor, 1961	

Table 4.2 continued

Location	Position ° '	Sur-face	Dates	Elev. m	Rad.	Conv.	Cond.	Reference	Note
Thule Ramp Greenland ice cap	76 24N 68 20W	snow/ice	6 July–28 Aug.	570	56	44		Schytt, 1955	5
Leirevag snowfield N. E. Greenland	74 25N 20 50W	snow	1–13 Aug.	5	52	34	14	Eriksson, 1942	
Fröya Glacier N. E. Greenland	74 24N 20 50W	snow	1–13 Aug.	450	8	83	9	Eriksson, 1942	
Greenland ice cap	69 40N 49 37W	ice	27 June–7 July	1000	86	14		Ambach, 1960	3
Sverdrup Glacier Devon Island	75 40N 83 15W	ice	9 July–10 Aug.	300	51	34	15	Keeler, 1964	
Barnes Ice Cap Baffin Island	70 14N 73 55W	snow	5 July–11 Aug.	1075	70	18	7	Sagar, 1966	6, 7
Barnes Ice Cap Baffin Island	70 14N 73 55W	snow	June–Aug.	1075	88	5	1	Sagar, 1966	2, 6, 8
Barnes Ice Cap Baffin Island	69 43N 72 13W	snow/ice	25 May–4 Aug.	865	68	32	0	Ward and Orvig, 1953	6
Penny Ice Cap Baffin Island	66 59N 65 28W	snow	13–26 July	2050	61	30	9	Orvig, 1954	
Karsa Glacier Sweden	68 20N 18 20E	snow	Aug.	above 1000	32	44	24	Wallen, 1948	

Table 4.2 continued

Location	Position ° ′	Surface	Dates	Elev. m.	Rad.	Conv.	Cond.	Reference	Note
Karsa Glacier Sweden	68 20N 18 20E	ice	Aug.	below 1000	55	29	16	Wallen, 1948	
Moscow Univ. Glacier Polar Urals, U.S.S.R	67 40N 66 E	snow/ice	21 July–3 Aug.	750	41	42	17	Lebedeva, 1960	
Hoffellsjökull Iceland	64 27N 15 30W	snow/ice	April–Oct.	200	14	86		Ahlmann and Thorarinsson, 1938	3, 4
Salmon Glacier Coast Mts., Canada	56 10N 130 07W	snow	30 July–9 Aug.	1700	75	15	10	Adkins, 1958	
Blue Glacier Olympic Mts., U.S.A.	47 48N 123 43W	snow	12 July–20 Aug.	2040	57	34	9	LaChapelle, 1959b	
Blue Glacier Olympic Mts., U.S.A.	47 48N 123 43W	snow	22 July–13 Aug.	2040	60	37	3	LaChapelle, 1960	2
Hornkees Austria	47 00N 11 50E	ice	3–9 Sept.	2260	53	35	12	Hoinkes, 1953	
Gepatschferner Austria	46 53N 10 45E	ice	8–16 Sept.	2300	65	35		Hoinkes, 1955	3
Kesselwandferner Austria	46 51N 10 47E	snow	11 Aug.–8 Sept.	3240	68	32		Ambach and Hoinkes, 1963	3

Table 4.2 continued

Location	Position ° '	Surface	Dates	Elev. m	Rad.	Conv.	Cond.	Reference	Note
Vernagtferner Austria	46 50N 10 45E	ice	21–31 Aug.	2970	79	18	3	Hoinkes and Untersteiner, 1952	
Vernagtferner Austria	46 50N 10 45E	ice	21 July–4 Aug.	2970	84	16		Hoinkes, 1955	2, 3
Central Tuyuksu Gl. Tien Shan, U.S.S.R.	43 N 77 E	snow/ice	10 July–9 Sept.	3475	78	22		Skeib, 1962	3
Hodges Glacier South Georgia	54 14S 36 35W	snow/ice	Nov.–April	450	35	35	30	Smith, 1960	

Notes:

1. Net loss of heat by convection observed here.
2. Measurements made at same place as last, but in different years.
3. "Convection" = convection + condensation.
4. Radiation was calculated, not measured, and "convection + condensation" obtained by subtracting radiation from the heat needed to produce the measured ablation.
5. "Convection" = convection + condensation — evaporation.
6. "Condensation" = condensation — evaporation.
7. Refreezing of rain supplied 5 per cent of heat.
8. Refreezing of rain supplied 6 per cent of heat.

ranges from 8 to 100 per cent, convection from 0 to 86 per cent, condensation from 0 to 30 per cent. Some of the variations doubtless reflect experimental inaccuracies and some arise because measurements only cover a small part of the season. But there are wide differences between different areas, even between areas where one might expect similar conditions. However, in twenty-four out of the thirty-two cases radiation supplied more than half the total heat, and in one other case it was the greatest of the three terms. Most of the places where convective heat exceeded radiation had snow surfaces and were at comparatively low elevations. Except in one case, condensation was the smallest term.

In short, the usual order of importance of the heat sources during the ablation season is radiation, convection, condensation. In some circumstances convection may be more important than radiation. It would be rash to attempt any more precise generalization than this. The data in Table 4·2 show little correlation between percentage of radiation and elevation, latitude, or distance from the sea. A detailed statistical analysis of all available data, subdivided according to time, weather conditions, nature of surface and so on, might reveal some correlations between results from different areas. However, energy balance studies have so far yielded detailed information only about the particular places where they were carried out.

CHAPTER 5

MEASUREMENTS RELATING TO GLACIER FLOW

"Be ye doers of the word and not hearers only"
Epistle of James.

Introduction

In a glacier or ice sheet the ice is deforming plastically as a result of stresses produced by its own weight. In addition the ice mass as a whole may be sliding over the underlying bedrock. These two processes, combined in places with faulting, constitute glacier movement.

The flow law of ice (the relation between the rate of deformation and the stress which produces it) can be determined in the laboratory. When the flow law is known, the methods of the mathematical theory of plasticity can be used to calculate the theoretical distribution of stresses and velocities in idealized glaciers of simple shapes. In this way a considerable body of theory has been built up during the past 15 years: this has greatly increased our understanding of glacier behaviour. Sliding of a glacier over its bed has also been studied, but the theory is less well developed.

Field measurements are required to test how well these theories apply to real glaciers. In this chapter we shall discuss the quantities which have to be determined in a detailed study of glacier flow, and outline methods of measuring them. We shall then quote some typical results. The theory will be given in subsequent chapters. However, certain features of the velocity distribution in a glacier can be deduced from simple considerations. This will be done now, as it should assist in an understanding of the experimental results.

Some General Aspects of Glacier Flow

In the upper part of a glacier, the amount of snow added to the surface each year exceeds the amount lost by melting, run-off and evaporation. In the lower part, some ice and all the previous winter's snow are lost each summer. The profile of the glacier does not change much from year to year, however, because ice flows from the "accumulation area" to the "ablation area".

Consider a cross-section through the glacier perpendicular to the surface and to the direction of flow. If the profile of the glacier is to remain unchanged, the amount of ice flowing, in a year, through any such cross-section in the accumulation area must equal the total amount of snow which has collected during the year on the area of the glacier above the cross-section. Similarly, in the ablation area, the amount of ice flowing through a cross-section in a year must equal the amount of ice lost from the glacier between the cross-section and the terminus. Thus, the amount of ice flowing through any cross-section must increase steadily from zero at the head of the glacier to a maximum at the "equilibrium line" (the boundary between accumulation and ablation areas) and from there decrease steadily to the terminus. We would expect the ice velocity to vary in a similar way, provided that the glacier's width and thickness do not change greatly throughout its length. Thus the ice velocity should be a maximum at the equilibrium line.

Moreover, if the elevation of the glacier surface at each point is to remain constant, the velocity vector cannot be parallel to the surface. The vector must be inclined downwards relative to the surface in the accumulation area and upwards in the ablation area. Thus we might expect the general pattern of flow lines in a glacier to be as shown in Fig. 5.1.

In a real glacier, variations in thickness, width, slope and other factors will produce many deviations from this simple flow pattern. Nevertheless, these are important ideas to keep in mind.

An important result from plasticity theory is that velocity is mainly determined by ice thickness and surface slope. Ice will flow in the direction of maximum surface slope even when this

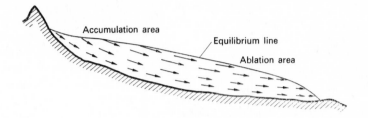

Fig. 5.1. Velocity vectors in ideal glacier.

corresponds to an uphill slope of the underlying bedrock. In this context "slope" means the average slope over a distance comparable with the ice thickness. Variations in surface slope over short distances, as occur on ice hummocks for example, have no effect on the flow of the glacier. Velocity is proportional to about the fourth power of ice thickness and to about the third power of surface slope. Another important result is that the product of thickness and surface slope does not vary much from place to place on a glacier, or even from one glacier to another. The ice is usually thin at places where the surface is steep, and thick where the slope is gentle.

Measurement of Velocity

We shall first discuss measurement of surface velocity. This merely involves standard surveying techniques. To specify the velocity vector completely we must determine the components parallel and perpendicular to the surface. In practice one measures the horizontal component and its direction and the vertical component. Measurements, by photogrammetry or other means, of the change in position of boulders, cracks, or other marks on the glacier surface only gives the horizontal velocity. Measurement of the vertical component requires the use of markers fixed in the ice. Wooden stakes set in holes drilled in the ice are commonly used. In the ablation area, the only problem is to

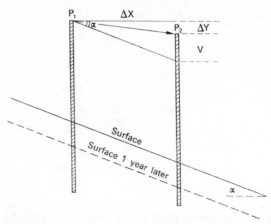

FIG. 5.2. The position of a stake set in the ice at two times, 1 year apart. Because the ice velocity vector is inclined upwards relative to the glacier surface, the vertical displacement ΔY of the top of the stake is less than $\Delta X \tan \alpha$ by an amount V, the "emergence velocity". (This refers to the ablation area.)

drill holes sufficiently deep that the stakes will not melt out during the summer. In the accumulation area, where the surface layers consist of snow and firn rather than ice, it is difficult to ensure that the stake is fixed rigidly enough for accurate measurement of the vertical velocity component. Indeed, few measurements of this component have been made in accumulation areas.

Measurement of the vertical component of velocity sometimes causes confusion. Consider first the situation on the centreline of the glacier where there is no cross-glacier component of velocity. Figure 5.2 shows a stake set in the ice. At time t the top of the stake is at P_1; one year later it is at P_2. The motion of the stake follows the velocity vector of the ice surrounding its base. (The diagram shows the vector inclined upwards relative to the surface. Thus it refers to the ablation area.) We measure the horizontal and vertical displacements ΔX and ΔY of the top of the stake, with respect to axes fixed in space. The horizontal velocity component U is equal to ΔX. If ice flow were parallel to the surface, ΔY would be equal to $\Delta X \tan \alpha$, where α is the surface slope. But ice flow is upwards relative to the surface. Thus the vertical displacement ΔY is less than $\Delta X \tan \alpha$ by an amount V. Here V is the thickness of ice (measured vertically) delivered to the glacier surface in unit time. It is the rate at which the surface would rise if there were no ablation. It is sometimes called the "emergence velocity". (In the accumulation area it is a "submergence velocity".) Thus

$$\Delta Y = \Delta X \tan \alpha - V$$
$$V = \Delta X \tan \alpha - \Delta Y$$

The component v perpendicular to the surface is often of more interest than the vertical component V. Normally v is measured positive downwards. Thus

$$v = -V \cos \alpha$$
$$v = \Delta Y \cos \alpha - \Delta X \sin \alpha$$

At a point off the centreline of the glacier, ΔX is equal to the component of horizontal velocity in the direction of the centreline. That is

$$U = \Delta X \sec \Delta A$$

where ΔA is the angle between the direction of horizontal velocity and the centreline.

Consider now the change in the ice surface at a point, such as a stake, which is moving with the ice. In one year the surface would rise by an amount v (measured perpendicular to the surface) if there were no ablation. But in fact ablation removes a layer of thickness b (mass balance expressed as ice thickness and measured perpendicular to the surface). The difference between the two is the annual change in ice thickness Δh at the stake. Thus

$$\Delta h = b - v$$

The distance from the top of the stake to the ice surface is measured at the beginning and end of the balance year. The difference is b. Thus Δh is determined from measurements of b and v.

In most cases b and v are approximately equal and their difference Δh is small.

The above discussion referred to the ablation area. The equations also apply to the accumulation area, although compaction of the upper layers of firn may complicate the measurements there.

To obtain a general idea of the flow of a glacier, it is best to set one line of stakes along the centreline. This can be supplemented by a few transverse lines. These should extend right to the edges of the glacier. In valley glaciers stations can be established on bedrock around the perimeter, and changes in positions of the stakes determined by repeated triangulation from these. This method is sufficiently accurate for measurements of horizontal velocities over periods of a few days or longer. The vertical velocity component is much smaller than the horizontal. Thus two measurements of the elevation of a marker must be separated by several months at least.

For measurements on ice caps it is not usually possible to establish triangulation stations on bedrock. Traverse methods have to be employed and electronic distance-measuring equipment is most useful. Markers on an ice cap should be arranged in lines at right angles to the contours. Such lines should correspond, at least approximately, to flow lines.

To measure surface movement of the central parts of the Greenland and Antarctic ice sheets the only feasible method at present is to make repeated astro-fixes. This only determines the horizontal component of velocity and, as the method is not very accurate, measurements have to be made over a period of several years.

Measurement of velocity at depth requires a borehole and so is a major undertaking. To date, most deep holes in glaciers have been made with thermal drills. Drilling speeds of a few metres per hour are typical. Thermal drilling is probably the simplest method if the ice is at the pressure melting temperature. In cold ice, however, the meltwater produced by the drill must be removed, otherwise it will refreeze and seize the drill. Thus much more elaborate equipment is needed. Boreholes in temperate glaciers must be cased to keep out water, otherwise the winter "cold wave" will freeze the water near the surface and block the hole. Apart from this, flow of ice at depth will close an uncased hole. In cold glaciers, closure is less rapid and there is no water in the body of the glacier. Thus it may be sufficient to case only the upper part of the hole. This prevents the entry of surface melt-water and also the caving in of snow or firn in an accumulation area.

The velocity at depth can be deduced from measurements with an inclinometer. This instrument determines the inclination of the axis of the borehole to the vertical, and the azimuth of this inclination. Measurements are made at different depths and repeated at intervals (usually one year). A plot of inclination versus depth at two different times determines the horizontal displacement of the borehole at different depths. This gives the relative horizontal component of ice velocity at these depths. To convert to absolute velocities, the displacement of the top of the borehole casing is measured by the survey techniques used for surface markers. The vertical component of velocity of the top of the casing is also measured by survey methods. There is, however, no way to find the vertical component of velocity at depth. Thus borehole measurements do not completely determine the velocity vector at depth.

Provided that the borehole reaches bedrock, this method also determines the rate at which the glacier is sliding over its bed.

Measurement of Strain Rate

In studies of flow, it is often more important to know the strain rates (that is, the velocity gradients) rather than the absolute velocities. For example, knowledge of surface strain rates is essential for a proper interpretation of borehole data in terms of the flow law of ice. Strain rates have not been measured on very many glaciers, however.

With a line of stakes down the centreline of the glacier, the longitudinal strain rate between adjacent stakes can be measured. (Change in distance between the two stakes in unit time, expressed as a fraction of the original distance.) However, it is preferable to determine all the components of strain rate at the surface. To do this, four stakes are set in the shape of a diamond with one diagonal in the direction of flow. The length of each side should be roughly equal to the ice thickness. One stake should also be placed at the centre of the diamond. The lengths of the sides and the diagonals are measured by steel tape or other means, and the measurements repeated a year later. From these data the longitudinal and transverse strain rates $\partial u/\partial x$, $\partial w/\partial z$, the shear strain rate $\frac{1}{2}$ $(\partial u/\partial z + \partial \omega/\partial x)$, and their standard errors, can be calculated by a least squares method. (Here the x coordinate is measured down the centreline of the glacier and the z coordinate across the glacier. The corresponding velocity components are u and w.) A paper by Nye (1959a) gives details of the calculations. The strain rate perpendicular to the glacier surface $\partial v/\partial y$ is difficult to measure. It is best obtained from the following relation, which holds because ice is incompressible.

$$\partial u/\partial x + \partial v/\partial y + \partial \omega/\partial z = 0$$

Measurement of Ice Thickness

In flow studies one must know the configuration of the glacier bed. Thus the ice thickness must be measured. Several methods are available and these will now be outlined. With one exception they are standard geophysical prospecting techniques.

Seismic sounding has been used extensively. A small charge is exploded at, or a short distance below, the glacier surface. The resulting compressional wave travels through the ice to the glacier bed and is reflected back to the surface. The travel time is measured accurately. If the velocity of the wave in the ice is known, the ice thickness can be calculated. The slope of the glacier bed can also be found if a multi-channel instrument is used. The velocity of seismic waves in the local ice is determined by measurements of refracted waves. The velocity depends on the ice temperature, among other factors. Typical values for compressional waves range from about 3·6 km sec $^{-1}$ in ice at the melting point to 3·9 km sec $^{-1}$ at $-45°C$ (Robin, 1958). Velocity also depends on density. Thus velocity varies with depth in the upper layers of the accumulation area. Ice thicknesses obtained by this method should normally be within a few metres of the true value.

Seismic sounding in the interior of Antarctica has proved difficult (Bentley, 1964). At low temperatures, a large part of the energy from a surface explosion is converted into surface waves which travel in the upper layers of firn. This appears as noise on the records and obscures the reflected wave. To overcome this problem, the charges have to be set at depths of about 50 m. Depths of a few metres have proved adequate in most other areas.

An alternative sounding technique is to measure variations in gravity. Such measurements give the ice thickness averaged over an area rather than at a point. The resulting profiles of the glacier bed are somewhat smoothed and the method cannot pick out minor irregularities.

The force of gravity at any point on the earth's surface depends mainly on the mass of material under that point. The density of ice is only about one third that of rock. Thus variations in ice thickness from place to place will produce variations in the measured value of gravity. These variations, though small, can be detected by modern gravimeters. As the value of gravity depends on elevation above sea level and on latitude, the elevation of the point must be determined to within a few metres and the latitude to within 1 min. If the glacier is not well mapped, this survey work may take much longer than the gravity measurements themselves, which are rapid and simple.

The measured value of gravity has also to be corrected for the effects of the topography within a radius of about 10 km. This correction can be very large for a glacier in a mountainous area, and an accurate map is then essential. The gravity method is more suitable for ice caps, where the terrain corrections are likely to be small. A good method on an ice cap is to make widely spaced seismic soundings and use gravity measurements to fill in the gaps.

Measurements of ice thickness by the gravity method should be accurate to 10 or 20 m.

Measurements of electrical resistivity have occasionally been used to determine ice thicknesses. An electric current, usually direct current, is passed through the ice and the underlying bedrock by two electrodes inserted in the glacier surface. The potential difference between two other surface electrodes is measured. This potential difference depends on the resistivity of the medium. In this case, the medium consists of two layers (ice and bedrock) and the measured resistivity is a combination of the two separate resistivities. The measured resistivity depends on the path of the current which in turn depends on the spacing of the electrodes. Measurements are made with several different spacings. A graph of measured resistivity against electrode spacing is then compared with theoretical curves for two-layered media of different thicknesses. In this way ice thickness can be determined.

Like the gravity method, resistivity measurements determine average ice thickness over an area. The resistivity method is the less accurate of the two. Resistivity depends on the temperature, and on certain other characteristics of the ice which have not yet been clearly identified. Once the method has been developed, it may prove more useful for obtaining information on the nature of the ice, rather than as a sounding technique.

Radar is a very promising new method for measuring the thickness of glaciers and ice sheets. The possibilities of this method first became apparent after several reports from Antarctica of errors in aircraft radar altimeters. The explanation was that part of the transmitted radio energy penetrated the ice and was reflected from the ice–rock interface at the bottom. These reflections were mistaken for reflections from the ice surface. The discrepancy cannot be interpreted directly as ice thickness however, because the velocity of radio waves in air is about 1·8 times their velocity in ice.

Absorption of radio waves by ice is sufficiently low that this is a feasible sounding technique. Absorption increases with temperature. Thus greater thicknesses can be measured in polar ice sheets than elsewhere. It may in fact be possible to deduce the ice temperature from measurements of the strength of the reflected signal. If the ice is wet, it reflects too much energy and the method becomes impracticable. The velocity of radio waves in ice varies little over the range of temperatures encountered. Velocity does depend on density, however. Thus some assumption about the variation of density with depth in the upper layers of firn is necessary, unless measurements are available. Thicknesses measured by radar should be accurate to about 10 m.

The first soundings were made with standard radar altimeters, but special radars have now been developed. The equipment can be mounted in either an aircraft or a surface vehicle. One great advantage of this method is that a continuous profile of the bottom of the glacier is obtained. Other methods merely give the thickness at isolated points (seismic) or smoothed profiles (gravity and resistivity). The radar, if mounted in an aircraft, also gives a profile of the surface of the glacier. As a result of these advantages, radar has now largely superseded other methods of sounding polar ice caps.

Results

In this section we shall discuss some typical measurements, mainly of velocities.

Glaciers vary in size from the Antarctic ice sheet to small patches of ice in mountain corries. The area of a corrie glacier may be less than 0.5 km^2 and the ice in it may be only a few tens of metres thick. Maximum thicknesses of the major glaciers in the Alps and in the Canadian Rockies are probably between 300 and 600 m. To quote two examples from other mountain areas, ice thicknesses of 700 m have been measured in Malaspina Glacier, Alaska and 1000 m in Fedtchenko Glacier in the Pamirs, U.S.S.R. The maximum thickness of the Greenland ice sheet is about 3000 m. The area of the Antarctic ice sheet, excluding the floating ice shelves, is approximately 12×10^6 km^2 or about 20 per cent greater than Europe. Its average thickness is about 1900 m; the maximum thickness measured so far is 4300 m.

Many velocity measurements have been made in ablation areas, but comparatively few in accumulation areas. South Cascade Glacier in northwestern U S.A. in one of the very few

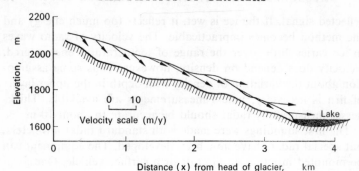

FIG. 5.3. Surface velocity vectors: South Cascade Glacier, U.S.A.
From Meier and Tangborn (1965).

glaciers for which a complete longitudinal velocity profile is
available. Figure 5.3 shows velocity vectors along the centreline,
as measured by Meier and Tangborn (1965).

The velocity distribution is much more complex than the simple
pattern in Fig. 5.1. There are three velocity maxima, at $x =$
0·9, 1·8, and 2·5 km. These correspond to maxima of surface
slope. In most years, the equilibrium line is in the vicinity of
$x = 2·2$ km which is near a velocity minimum. However, the
glacier is wide and deep there, so that the volume of ice passing
through this cross-section is relatively high even though the
velocity u is small. The general trend is for u to increase with x in
the accumulation area, as expected. And in the lower part of the
ablation area, u decreases as x increases. The velocity is not zero
at the terminus, even though the glacier has been retreating for
many years. This situation is not unusual. Advance or retreat of a
glacier is determined by the difference between the forward velocity at the terminus, and the loss of ice by melting or calving
there. (In glaciers in which the main loss of ice is by calving, the
equilibrium line may be near the terminus. In this case the velocity at the terminus may be near the maximum value. Many
Antarctic glaciers are in this category.)

The maximum velocity of South Cascade Glacier is about
20 m y $^{-1}$, a very low value. Most valley glaciers have velocities
in the range 10 to 200 m y $^{-1}$ for most of their length; but the

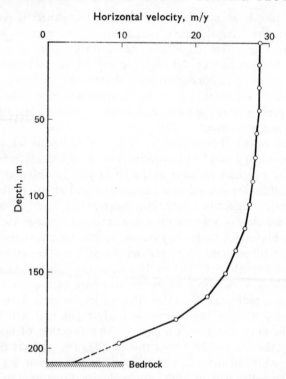

FIG. 5.4. Variation of horizontal velocity with depth: Athabasca Glacier, Canada. From Savage and Paterson (1963).

velocity may reach 1 or 2 km y^{-1} in icefalls. Measured velocities of the large glaciers which drain the Antarctic ice sheet range from 300 to 1400 m y^{-1}. A velocity of 10 km y^{-1} has been measured near the calving terminus of Jakobshavn Glacier, one of the largest outlet glaciers from the Greenland ice sheet. In glacier "surges", described in Chapter 8, movements of 4 to 7 km in a few months have been recorded.

Figure 5.3 shows that velocity vectors on South Cascade Glacier are inclined downwards relative to the surface in the accumulation area and upwards in the ablation area. (The equi-

6*

librium line is at $x = 2.2$ km.) This is the expected pattern. Note that the vertical scale is exaggerated. The vectors are inclined at only a few degrees to the surface. This is normal: vertical components of velocity are usually about an order of magnitude less than horizontal ones. Vectors may be more steeply inclined near the sides of a glacier than elsewhere. Ablation may also be greater near the sides, as a result of heat radiated by the valley walls in summer.

Typical values of emergence velocity v in temperate regions are of the order of 1 m y^{-1} (downwards) in accumulation areas and 3 or 4 m y^{-1} and perhaps up to 10 m y^{-1} in ablation areas. As the values are related to accumulation and ablation, they are considerably higher in a maritime climate than in arctic regions.

The variation of velocity on a line across the glacier is also of interest. Figure 6.6 (page 108) shows the down-glacier component of horizontal velocity on a transverse line. These measurements were made by Meier (1960) on Saskatchewan Glacier in Canada. The velocity varies little in the central part of the glacier and decreases rapidly near the sides. This pattern is typical, provided the cross-section of the channel is fairly regular. It will be discussed in more detail in Chapter 6. The direction of flow was virtually the same right across this profile. This reflects the fact that the width of the valley is constant in this region. At places where the valley widens in the down-glacier direction, horizontal velocity vectors off the centreline diverge slightly towards each side of the glacier. Conversely, these vectors are inclined towards the centreline at places where the valley becomes narrower in the down-glacier direction.

Figure 5.4 shows a typical curve of velocity versus depth. Savage and Paterson (1963) obtained these data from a borehole in Athabasca Glacier, Canada. This borehole, which reached bedrock, was near the centreline in the ablation area. Velocity varies little with depth in the upper half of the borehole; in the lower half, velocity decreases and at an increasing rate as the bottom is approached. The sliding velocity is only about 10 per cent of the surface velocity.

Very few measurements of sliding velocity have been made.

TABLE 5.1. RATIO OF VELOCITY AT GLACIER BED TO VELOCITY AT SURFACE

Glacier	Country	Velocity ratio	Ice thickness (metres)	Reference
Aletsch	Switzerland	0·5	137	Gerrard and others, 1952
Tuyuksu	U.S.S.R.	0·65	52	Vilesov, 1961
Salmon	Canada	0·45	495	Mathews, 1959
Athabasca	Canada	0·75	322	Savage and Paterson, 1963
Athabasca	Canada	0·10	209	Savage and Paterson, 1963
Blue*	U.S.A.	0·9	26	Kamb and LaChapelle, 1964
Skautbre*	Norway	0.9	50	McCall, 1952

* These measurements were made in a tunnel, not a borehole.

The only ones known to the author are listed in Table 5.1. These data indicate that, on the average, sliding comprises roughly half the total movement. This applies to glaciers in which the basal ice is at the pressure melting temperature. It is believed that glaciers in which the basal ice is below the melting point do not slip on their beds. Table 5.1 also shows that large variations can occur over comparatively short distances. The two boreholes in Athabasca Glacier were only 1·5 km apart, and on the same flow line. In one case sliding accounted for 75 per cent of the movement; in the other, only 10 per cent.

In addition to all the glaciers listed in Table 5.1, deep boreholes have been drilled in the following glaciers in recent years: Isfalls (Sweden), Austerdals (Norway), Saskatchewan (Canada), Taku and Malaspina (Alaska, U.S.A.) The majority of these boreholes did not reach bedrock and no velocity data have been published for the ones that did. Deep boreholes have also been drilled in the Greenland and Antarctic ice sheets. These have yielded data on ice temperatures and borehole closure rates, and have provided samples of ice. But no differential movement at depth has so far been recorded in them.

We have described the main features of the variation of glacier velocity in space. Let us now look briefly at how the velocity varies with time. Numerous observers have noted that the velocity at a point on a glacier is not constant throughout the year. In this context a "point" means a point fixed relative to the glacier bed. We have seen that the velocity of a point moving with the ice is likely to decrease as it approaches the terminus. This is not what is meant by a variation of velocity with time.

Results show that, in general, the variations become larger as the time interval over which the velocity is measured is reduced (Meier, 1960). For example, average summer and winter velocities may differ from each other by 10 or 20 per cent. Measurements from month to month may vary by perhaps 40 per cent during a year. Fluctuations of 100 per cent or more have been observed in measurements made every few hours. This trend is not merely a reflection of the increasing effect of experimental errors as the time interval is reduced, although to make reliable measurements over intervals of a day or less is very difficult. Measurements over periods of a few hours suggest that movement at each point proceeds in a series of small jerks and that the jerks at different points are not synchronized. Such behaviour is not surprising in crevassed areas, but apparently it may occur elsewhere as well. The great majority of measured velocities are averages over periods of weeks or months, in which these discontinuities are smoothed out.

There are two possible explanations of seasonal changes in velocity. First, they may result from changes of ice thickness. Accumulation and ablation produce variations in thickness of a few per cent during the year. As velocity is proportional to approximately the fourth power of the thickness, variations of up to 15 or 20 per cent may be explained in this way. Velocity should be a maximum in late spring and a minimum at the end of summer. The other explanation involves the "lubricating" effect of meltwater at the glacier bed. (This is discussed in detail in Chapter 7.) In this case the sliding velocity should be a maximum when the amount of meltwater at the glacier bed is a maximum, namely in the middle of the ablation season. A velocity maximum has often been observed then. Observations of temporary increases in velocity after heavy rain might also be explained in this way. This second explanation cannot apply in glaciers which are frozen to their beds. In other glaciers, changes in velocity may result from a combination of the two effects. The amplitude of the fluctuations, and the time of year when the velocity is greatest, are two criteria for deciding which effect is more important in any particular glacier.

Variations of velocity with periods of many years are also observed. These represent the response of the glacier to climatically-induced changes in its mass balance. This forms the subject of Chapter 11.

Figure 5.3 (page 74.), which shows the variation of velocity u with distance x along the centreline of South Cascade Glacier, can also be interpreted in terms of longitudinal strain rate $\partial u/\partial x$. At most places in the accumulation area $\partial u/\partial x$ is positive. However, it is negative around $x = 1 \cdot 1$ km and again between $x = 1 \cdot 9$ and $x = 2 \cdot 0$ km. This strain rate is positive between $x = 2 \cdot 1$ and $x = 2 \cdot 5$ km, a region which includes the upper part of the ablation area. However, this strain rate is negative in the remainder of the ablation area. As velocity is expected to be a maximum at the equilibrium line, the longitudinal strain rate should be mainly positive in the accumulation area, and mainly negative in the ablation area.

An area where $\partial u/\partial x$ is positive is often referred to as a region of *extending flow*. Similarly flow is often said to be *compressing* where $\partial u/\partial x$ is negative. These expressions may seem peculiar at first sight, because ice is an incompressible solid except in so far as included air bubbles can be reduced in size. "Compressing" merely refers to a reduction of the length of a block of ice in the x direction. This must be accompanied by a corresponding increase in its height or width. As the valley walls prevent lateral expansion, the glacier thickness must increase in the down-glacier direction in a region of compressing flow. In this case there must be a velocity component upwards relative to the surface (the "emergence velocity"). In practice, this thickening is counteracted by ablation, as explained previously.

Further Reading

A paper by Meier (1960) is a good example of detailed measurements of flow in a valley glacier. Further details of the various techniques for measuring ice thickness can be found in papers by Doell (1963) (seismic), Corbato (1965) (gravity), Greenhouse (1961) (resistivity) and Evans (1963) (radar).

CHAPTER 6

GLACIER FLOW I: ICE DEFORMATION

"Science moves, but slowly slowly,
Creeping on from point to point"

TENNYSON, *Locksley Hall.*

Introduction

Fundamental to all theoretical treatments of glacier flow is the flow law of ice, that is, the relation between deformation and the stress which produces it. For many years ice was assumed to behave like a fluid of very high, but constant, viscosity. In a fluid, strain rate is directly proportional to stress. However, the velocity of a glacier appeared to be more sensitive to small changes in thickness than this law predicted.

About 1948, it was realized that, as ice is a polycrystalline solid, it might be expected to deform in a similar way to other polycrystalline solids such as metals, rather than as a fluid. This may seem obvious now, but it was a major advance at that time. Laboratory experiments confirmed that ice does indeed behave like metals at temperatures not far below their melting points. A continued stress produces permanent deformation. Initially, application of stress results in deformation at a changing rate. If the stress remains constant, the deformation rate eventually reaches a steady value however. With this flow law as a basis, Nye calculated the distribution of stress and velocity in idealized glaciers of simple shapes. These theoretical studies have been conspicuously successful in explaining many observed features of glacier flow.

We shall first describe the results of laboratory measurements. We shall then discuss how these results can be generalized for complex stress systems such as exist in glaciers. Nye's theoretical work will then be outlined. The processes by which a glacier slips on its bed will be dealt with in the next chapter. Special questions relating to flow in a large ice sheet are postponed until Chapter 9. The distinction between glaciers and ice sheets in this context is rather artificial, however. Many of the results derived in the present chapter apply to ice sheets as well.

The Flow Law of Ice

Numerous laboratory experiments have been made to determine the flow law of ice, for both single crystals and polycrystalline aggregates. Glen (1958a) has summarized the results. While some details of the mechanism of flow remain uncertain, the general features are now well established. For our purposes, the mathematical form of the law is more important than details of the mechanism.

A single crystal deforms plastically by the gliding, one over another, of layers parallel to the basal plane (see Chapter 2). No "yield stress", below which no deformation takes place, has been found. Normal practice is to apply a constant shear stress and measure the variation of strain with time. For a given stress, the strain rate initially increases with time, but settles down to a steady value after a few hours. This type of behaviour is called "creep".

The relation between the final strain rate $\dot{\varepsilon}_{xy}$ and the shear stress τ_{xy} across the basal plane is

$$\dot{\varepsilon}_{xy} = A\,\tau_{xy}^n \qquad (1)$$

where A and n are constants. The value of A depends on the temperature; that of n does not. Values of n obtained by different experimenters range from 1·5 to 3·9 with a mean of about 2·5. The flow of ice thus differs markedly from that of a viscous fluid for which n would equal 1, and A^{-1} would be the coefficient of viscosity. Experiments by Rigsby (1958) demonstrated the important result that hydrostatic pressure does not affect the flow law, provided that temperature is measured relative to the freezing point. Hydrostatic pressure does of course depress the freezing point.

Deformation of polycrystalline ice, such as occurs in glaciers, depends on the shape and orientation of the individual crystals. Several workers have studied this deformation under uniaxial compression or tension, as well as under simple shear. In the initial transient stage of deformation of randomly-oriented polycrystals, under constant stress, the strain rate decreases with time. Thereafter the strain rate reaches a steady value. However, at higher stresses, it may finally start to increase again. The initial decrease can be ascribed to interference between crystals with different orientations. Production, by recrystallization, of crystals more favourably oriented for glide in the direction of the stress, causes the final increase of strain rate.

The flow law of randomly-oriented polycrystalline ice is of the same form as that of single crystals. Hydrostatic pressure again has no effect on it. However, the value of A for polycrystals is only about 10^{-2} times that for single crystals. This can be attributed to most crystals being unfavourably oriented for glide in the direction of the applied stress.

As stated earlier, the value of A depends on the temperature. Glen (1955) showed that his data fitted Boltzmann's law, namely $\exp(-Q/RT)$. Here T is absolute temperature, R is the gas constant (8.31×10^7 erg deg^{-1}) and Q can be regarded as an activation energy for creep. Glen obtained a value of 31.8×10^3 cal mole^{-1} for Q. More recent measurements (Raraty and Tabor 1958) suggest 14×10^3 cal mole^{-1}. The latter figure implies that at a temperature of $-22°C$, the strain rate produced by a given stress is one-tenth of its value at $0°C$.

Measured values of n for polycrystalline ice vary between 1.9 and 4.5 with a mean of about 3. These values refer to the steady part of the creep curve. They exclude the initial transient part and also any final reacceleration under high stress. As stresses in glaciers act for very long periods, the transient stage is of no interest. However, stresses in some parts of glaciers may be large enough for the reacceleration to occur. At such places the appropriate value of n may be somewhat greater than 3. Most laboratory experiments have been performed with stresses between 0.5 and about 15 bars (1 bar $= 10^6$ dynes cm$^{-2} = 1.02$

kg cm $^{-2}$). Shear stresses in glaciers seldom exceed 1·5 bars. Thus, while the upper part of the stress range has been well covered, extrapolation of the laboratory results to lower stresses is necessary. There are some indications that the value of n should be reduced to about 2 or even 1 for stresses below about 0·9 bar (Butkovich and Landauer, 1960). Again, in theoretical studies, glacier ice is assumed to be isotropic. But, as described in Chapter 2, crystals of glacier ice may show preferred orientations. This casts doubt on whether a flow law for randomly-oriented crystals can be strictly applied to a glacier. However, many more samples of ice from depth must be studied before this question can be decided. Development of a preferred orientation in the direction of the stress would effectively increase the value of n.

In glacier studies, the flow law is generally assumed to have the form of equation (1) with n equal to 3. The preceding discussion has shown that to take the same value of n for all points on a glacier is only an approximation. However, calculations based on it have agreed satisfactorily with many field measurements.

The Generalized Flow Law

In practically all the laboratory experiments uniaxial compression or tension, or simple shear, was applied. Stress systems in glaciers are complex and the simple flow law has to be generalized. Nye (1957) has discussed how to do this.

Direct stresses are denoted by σ_x, σ_y, σ_z, shear stresses by τ_{xy}, τ_{yz}, τ_{zx}, and strain rates by $\dot{\varepsilon}_x$, $\dot{\varepsilon}_y$, $\dot{\varepsilon}_z$, $\dot{\varepsilon}_{xy}$, $\dot{\varepsilon}_{yz}$, $\dot{\varepsilon}_{zx}$.

Experiments show that the flow law is unaffected by hydrostatic pressure. The best way to express this is to work with stress deviators rather than stresses. The stress deviators are obtained by subtracting the hydrostatic pressure from the direct stresses. Thus

$$\sigma_x' = \sigma_x - \tfrac{1}{3}\left(\sigma_x + \sigma_y + \sigma_z\right) \qquad (2)$$

and similarly for σ_y', σ_z'. The shears are unchanged. A flow law which relates strain rates to stress deviators is unaffected by hydrostatic pressure.

A flow law for complex stress systems must be a relation between quantities which describe the overall state of stress and strain rate. Moreover, the flow law, which is a physical property of the material, cannot be affected by the way in which the coordinate axes are drawn.

To proceed further, two assumptions are made.

1. At any point, the strain rates are parallel to and proportional to the corresponding stress deviators. This is a reasonable assumption for an isotropic material, as ice is assumed to be. Thus

$$\dot{\varepsilon}_x = \lambda\sigma'_x \qquad \dot{\varepsilon}_{xy} = \lambda\tau_{xy} \tag{3}$$

and similar relations. The factor λ is a function of position, not a constant. By the definition of the stress deviators, as in (2)

$$\sigma'_x + \sigma'_y + \sigma'_z = 0 \tag{4}$$

and so from (3)

$$\dot{\varepsilon}_x + \dot{\varepsilon}_y + \dot{\varepsilon}_z = 0 \tag{5}$$

The strain rates in any incompressible material obey this last relation.

2. Nye proposed using the quantities $\dot{\varepsilon}$, τ, which he called the *effective strain rate* and the *effective shear stress*, defined by

$$2\dot{\varepsilon}^2 = \dot{\varepsilon}_x^2 + \dot{\varepsilon}_y^2 + \dot{\varepsilon}_z^2 + 2(\dot{\varepsilon}_{xy}^2 + \dot{\varepsilon}_{yz}^2 + \dot{\varepsilon}_{zx}^2) \tag{6}$$

$$2\tau^2 = \sigma'^2_x + \sigma'^2_y + \sigma'^2_z + 2(\tau_{xy}^2 + \tau_{yz}^2 + \tau_{zx}^2) \tag{7}$$

where $\dot{\varepsilon}$ and τ are both positive. It can be shown that values of $\dot{\varepsilon}$ and τ are unaffected by any rotation of the coordinate axes. The flow law is postulated to be a relation of the form

$$\dot{\varepsilon} = f(\tau)$$

or, in this particular case,

$$\dot{\varepsilon} = A\tau^n \tag{8}$$

where A, n have the values determined for randomly-oriented polycrystals in simple shear.

From (3), (6) and (7) it follows that

$$\dot{\varepsilon} = \lambda\tau \tag{9}$$

and by (8)

$$\lambda = A\tau^{n-1} \tag{10}$$

Thus by (3), relations between individual strain rates and stress deviators are of the form

$$\dot{\varepsilon}_x = A\tau^{n-1}\,\sigma_x' \qquad \dot{\varepsilon}_{xy} = A\tau^{n-1}\,\tau_{xy} \tag{11}$$

(Readers familiar with tensors will realize $2\dot{\varepsilon}^2$ and $2\tau^2$ are the second invariants of the strain rate and stress deviator tensors. The most general relation between two such tensors will involve their first, second, and third invariants. In the present case, the first invariants are zero by (4) and (5). Nye's formulation of the flow law involves only the second invariants. A more general law would involve the third invariants as well. Glen (1958b) has discussed this point.)

Let us consider two special cases. First, simple shear where $\dot{\varepsilon}_{xy}$, τ_{xy} are the only non-zero components. In this case $\dot{\varepsilon} = \dot{\varepsilon}_{xy}$ and $\tau = \tau_{xy}$ by (6) and (7). The general flow law (8) reduces to the flow law (1) for simple shear, as is necessary for consistency.

Now consider uniaxial compression or tension where σ_x is the only non-zero stress. In this case the general flow law reduces to

$$(\sqrt{3}/2)\,\dot{\varepsilon}_x = A(\sigma_x/\sqrt{3})^n$$

or, if $n = 3$,

$$\dot{\varepsilon}_x = \tfrac{2}{9}\,A\sigma_x^3$$

Comparison of this last equation with (1) shows that the strain rate produced by a given longitudinal tension (or compression) is only about 0·2 times that produced by an equal shear stress. This has been confirmed experimentally, which suggests that Nye's generalization of the flow law is a valid one.

However, to test the generalized law properly, ice must be subjected to a combination of stresses. Only two experimenters have done this. Steinemann (1958b) tested a block of ice in simultaneous shear and compression. Results suggested that (8) was not strictly accurate (Glen, 1958b). However, results of Voytkovskiy's (1960) experiments agreed with (8), within the limits of experimental error.

Nye's formulation is the simplest, but not the only possible, generalization of the flow law. The experimental evidence suggests that it is at least a reasonable approximation. In any case, use of a more complicated flow law would hardly be worth while, in view of other uncertainties in extrapolating laboratory results to conditions in glaciers. We shall now consider a few aspects of this flow law.

One most important feature is that, as (11) shows, each component of strain rate is proportional, not only to the corresponding stress deviator, but also to approximately the square of the effective shear stress. This last quantity is an increasing function of each stress deviator. Thus a stress acting by itself will produce a smaller strain rate than it would in the presence of other stresses.

For example, a tunnel dug in a glacier will close up under the pressure of the ice above it. At the foot of an icefall there is a large longitudinal compressive stress in the ice. Thus a tunnel there should close much more rapidly than it would at the same depth in a part of the glacier where other stresses are small. This has been confirmed on Austerdalsbre in Norway (Glen, 1958b). Again, crevasses, waves or large hummocks on the glacier surface tend to disappear due to the flow of ice under its own weight. This should happen more rapidly at the foot of an icefall than elsewhere.

In addition, the presence of additional stresses may effectively change the form of the relation between a strain rate and the corresponding stress deviator. For example, if τ_{xy} is the only non-zero stress deviator, $\tau = \tau_{xy}$ and equation (11), with $n = 3$, shows that $\dot{\varepsilon}_{xy}$ varies as τ_{xy}^3. However, if there is a longitudinal stress deviator σ_x' which is large compared with τ_{xy}, τ will be approximately equal to σ_x' and $\dot{\varepsilon}_{xy}$ will be proportional to $\sigma_x'^2 \tau_{xy}$. Thus $\dot{\varepsilon}_{xy}$ now varies linearly with τ_{xy}. This illustrates the complicated effects of a non-linear flow law.

Perfect Plasticity

We shall now introduce an important approximate form of the flow law. In Fig. 6.1, curve A is the relation

$$\dot{\varepsilon}_{xy} = A\, \tau_{xy}^n \tag{1}$$

Here $\dot{\varepsilon}_{xy}$ is shear strain rate in years^{-1} and τ_{xy} is shear stress in bars. Glen's values of the constants, namely $n = 4\cdot2$, $A = 0\cdot148$ y^{-1} bar$^{-4\cdot2}$, have been used. Curve B, a vertical straight line at $\tau = 1$ bar, is an approximation to curve A. Curve B implies that there is no deformation as long as the stress is less than 1 bar.

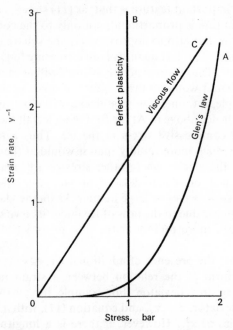

FIG. 6.1. Different types of relation between strain rate and stress.

When the stress reaches 1 bar the strain rate becomes very large. A material which behaves in this way is said to be *perfectly plastic* with a *yield stress* of 1 bar. The difference between ice and such a material is important in theory. Laboratory experiments have never shown that ice has a yield stress: the lowest stresses used have always produced some deformation. However, in practice, if the stress is much less than 1 bar, the deformation is small. If a stress much greater than 1 bar is applied for a long time, as it would be in a glacier, the final deformation is large. (For example, according to Fig. 6.1, a stress of 1·6 bars applied for 1 year produces a deformation of 100 per cent.) Thus, to regard ice as a perfectly plastic material with a yield stress of about 1 bar may be an adequate approximation for some purposes. The first step after abandoning the viscous law (curve C in Fig. 6.1) was to treat ice in this way (Nye, 1951). The laboratory flow law has been used in subsequent work however.

Mathematically, the case of perfect plasticity is obtained by letting $n \to \infty$ in (1). For, if we write $A = \tau_0^{-n}$, equation (1) becomes

$$\dot{\varepsilon}_{xy} = (\tau/\tau_0)^n$$

If $n \to \infty$, $\qquad \dot{\varepsilon}_{xy} \to 0 \qquad \tau < \tau_0$

$$\dot{\varepsilon}_{xy} \to \infty \qquad \tau > \tau_0$$

This corresponds to perfect plasticity with a yield stress of τ_0.

Laminar Flow

In Chapter 5 we described the main features of the velocity field in a glacier from a purely experimental standpoint. This approach, although often adopted, is not very satisfactory. It should be possible to explain such observations in terms of the flow properties of ice. The procedure is to consider blocks of ice of simple shapes as idealized models of glaciers. The stresses necessary to maintain the mechanical equilibrium of the block can be calculated. (Stresses in real glaciers have to be obtained by calculation in the same way. They have never been measured directly; it is difficult to see how this could be done.) Strain rates and velocities are derived from the stresses by means of the flow law. The theoretical velocity field can then be compared with observations.

Each model tells us something about conditions in a glacier. We do not expect that any one model will necessarily apply at a particular point in a real glacier. At some points we may have to adopt certain features of different models. And there will be many places where no simple model will apply at all.

One further limitation concerns the ice temperature. The factor

A in the flow law depends on temperature. Thus in general, A is a function of position. Moreover, the flow of ice is a means of heat transfer within the glacier. Thus the flow of mass and heat interact on each other. A general analysis would deal with both processes simultaneously. This would be very complicated and no one has yet attempted it. The simplest approach, and the one we shall adopt, is to assume that the temperature (relative to the pressure melting point) is constant throughout the glacier. The

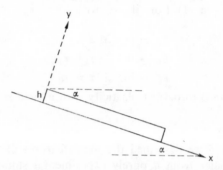

FIG. 6.2. Coordinate system for parallel-sided slab.

only real glaciers in which this is true are those which are at the pressure melting point, the so-called temperate glaciers. The theory can be extended to other glaciers by using, at each point, a flow law with parameter A appropriate to the temperature there.

As a first model of a glacier, consider a parallel-sided slab of ice of thickness h, resting on a rough plane of slope α (Fig. 6.2). The length and width of the slab are large compared with h. It is assumed that the slab does not slide on the plane: movement consists only of deformation within the slab due to its weight.

Consider a column of ice perpendicular to the plane and of unit cross-section. The weight of the column has component $\varrho g h \sin \alpha$ parallel to the plane. (Here ϱ is density and g is acceleration due to gravity.) This component of the weight is balanced by the shear stress τ_b across the base of the column. Thus

$$\tau_b = \varrho g h \sin \alpha \qquad (12)$$

This important formula has several implications:

1. The value of τ_b can be calculated from measurements of ice thickness h and surface slope α. This has been done for many glaciers. The great majority of values are between 0·5 and 1·5 bars. This shows that it is a reasonable approximation to regard ice as a perfectly plastic material with a yield stress of 1 bar.

2. If we assume perfect plasticity, we can write

$$h = \tau_0/\varrho g \sin \alpha$$

where τ_0 is 1 bar. From this formula, a rough estimate of ice thickness can be obtained from measurements of surface slope only. (We shall see later that, for a valley glacier, a factor in the range 0·5 to 0·8 should be inserted in the denominator on the right-hand side.)

3. The last formula implies that $h \sin \alpha$ is constant. Thus a glacier will be relatively thin where the surface is steep, and thick where the surface slope is small.

4. In the perfectly plastic model, the stress only reaches the yield stress at the base of the slab. Thus all the deformation occurs in the lowest layer. In a real glacier, the velocity varies with depth. Use of the true flow law enables us to derive this result (Nye, 1952a).

Take x axis in the plane, positive down-slope, and y axis perpendicular to the plane, positive upwards. Let u be the x component of velocity. It is assumed that the slab deforms in simple shear. Thus the flow lines are parallel to the surface of the slab. In this case flow is said to be *laminar*. It follows that the y component of velocity is zero and $\dot{\varepsilon}_{xy} = \frac{1}{2} du/dy$. For simple shear, the flow law reduces to the form (1), so that

$$\tfrac{1}{2}\, du/dy = A\tau_{xy}^n$$

By the argument used to derive (12), the shear stress τ_{xy} at depth $(h-y)$ below the surface of the slab is

$$\tau_{xy} = \varrho g(h-y) \sin \alpha \tag{12'}$$

It follows that

$$u_s - u_b = 2A(\varrho g)^n \sin^n \alpha \int_0^h (h-y)^n \, dy$$

$$u_s - u_b = 2A(\varrho g)^n (\sin^n \alpha) h^{n+1}/(n+1) \tag{13}$$

Here u_s and u_b are the velocities at the surface and base. In general, the velocity of sliding on the base, u_b, will not be zero. The present theory deals only with differential motion in the ice, $u_s - u_b$, and gives no information about u_b itself. If $u_b = 0$ and $n = 3$, we obtain the result, quoted in Chapter 5, that u_s is proportional to h^4 and to α^3. (At most places in a glacier, α is small and so $\sin \alpha \approx \alpha$.)

The velocity u at distance y above the base is given by

$$u_s - u = 2A(\varrho g)^n (\sin^n \alpha) (h-y)^{n+1}/(n+1) \tag{14}$$

This shows that the velocity is a maximum at the surface and decreases steadily with depth.

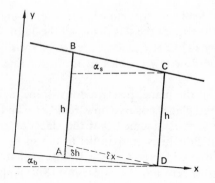

FIG. 6.3. Equilibrium of wedge-shaped block of ice.

The next step is to consider the situation when the surface of the slab is not parallel to its base (Nye, 1952b). Let α_s, α_b be the slopes. We assume that they are small. Take x, y axes as before. In Fig. 6.3, AB and CD are perpendicular to the base and distance δx apart. Consider the equilibrium of an element $ABCD$ of unit thickness in the direction normal to the xy plane. It is assumed that at each point in the slab there is a hydrostatic pressure equal to the weight of the overlying ice. This should be a reasonable assumption on the present model, except near the surface. Thus the normal pressure on AB is approximately equal to the hydrostatic pressure, the mean value of which is $\frac{1}{2} \varrho gh$, where $AB = h$. The normal force on AB is thus $\frac{1}{2} \varrho gh^2$. The normal force on CD is thus $\frac{1}{2} \varrho gh^2 - d/dx(\frac{1}{2} \varrho gh^2) \; \delta x$. The difference between the two is $- \varrho gh \; dh/dx \; \delta x$. Other forces parallel to the base are the component of the weight $\varrho gh \sin \alpha_b \cdot \delta x$ downhill, and $\tau_b \delta x$ uphill, where τ_b is the shear stress exerted by the bed on the ice. Thus for equilibrium

$$- \varrho gh \frac{dh}{dx} \delta x + \varrho gh \sin \alpha_b \, \delta x = \tau_b \, \delta x$$

But $dh/dx = \alpha_b - \alpha_s$ and $\sin \alpha_b = \alpha_b$ for small angles.

Thus $$\tau_b = \varrho gh \alpha_s$$

Thus τ_b is the same as if the slab had parallel sides of slope α_s.

Thus the shear stress at the bed is determined by the surface slope. Ice should flow in the direction of maximum surface slope even though the bed slopes in the opposite direction. This agrees with observation. Glacial valleys are often "over-deepened" at some distance from the terminus. For example, Malaspina Glacier is a large piedmont glacier in south-east Alaska whose terminus is about 1 km from the Pacific Ocean. Seismic measurements showed that the glacier bed is about 250 m below sea level some 15 km from the terminus. The glacier must therefore flow uphill for the last part of its course.

Extending and Compressing Flow

So far we have not considered any variation of velocity u with distance x along the glacier. In practice u does of course vary with x. We saw in Chapter 5 that, as a general trend, $\partial u/\partial x$ is positive in the accumulation area and negative in the ablation area. Thus we now obtain a more general solution that the one for laminar flow. The analysis follows that of Nye (1957).

The model is again a parallel-sided slab of ice, of thickness h, resting on a rough plane of slope α. The length and width of the slab are large compared with h. It is now convenient to take the origin on the surface of the slab. The x-axis lies in the surface, pointing down the direction of maximum slope; the y-axis is perpendicular to the surface, positive downwards; the z-axis is chosen to make the system right-handed. The velocity components are u, v, w. The density of the ice is ϱ, assumed for simplicity to be constant. The theory is easily modified to allow ϱ and the flow law to vary with y.

Use of a very wide slab implies that the influence of the valley walls on the flow of the glacier is neglected, and that we can assume that flow is confined to the xy plane. Thus all strain rates which involve z are zero. Equations (11) then show that all stress deviators involving z are also zero. In particular, $\sigma'_z = 0$ which implies that $2\sigma_z = \sigma_x + \sigma_y$

and, by (2) $\qquad \sigma'_x = -\sigma'_y = \frac{1}{2}(\sigma_x - \sigma_y)$

Also, by (7) $\qquad 4\tau^2 = (\sigma_x - \sigma_y)^2 + 4\tau_{xy}^2 \qquad (15)$

Moreover, since all strain rates which involve z are zero, by (6)

$$2\dot{\varepsilon}^2 = \left(\frac{\partial u}{\partial x}\right)^2 + \left(\frac{\partial v}{\partial y}\right)^2 + \frac{1}{2}\left(\frac{\partial u}{\partial y} + \frac{\partial v}{\partial x}\right)^2 \qquad (16)$$

and by (5) $\qquad\qquad \dfrac{\partial u}{\partial x} + \dfrac{\partial v}{\partial y} = 0 \qquad (17)$

Equations (11) now become

$$\left.\begin{array}{l} \dot{\varepsilon}_x = \partial u/\partial x = A\tau^{n-1}\,\sigma'_x \\[4pt] \dot{\varepsilon}_{xy} = \frac{1}{2}\,(\partial u/\partial y + \partial v/\partial x) = A\tau^{n-1}\,\tau_{xy} \end{array}\right\} \qquad (18)$$

To obtain an analytical solution, a further simplifying assumption is necessary. All stresses are assumed to be independent of x. This is plausible for a long, parallel-sided slab of constant slope. It follows from (18) that strain rates are also independent of x.

Thus

$$\left.\begin{array}{l} \partial^2 u/\partial x^2 = 0 \\ \partial^2 u/\partial x\,\partial y + \partial^2 v/\partial x^2 = 0 \end{array}\right\} \tag{19}$$

To obtain boundary conditions we note that there can be no shear stress on the free surface of the slab. Hence by (18) $\dot{\varepsilon}_{xy}$ must also be zero there. Also, provided that ice is not melting at the base of the slab, the velocity component v must be zero there. The solution of (17) and (19) which satisfies these boundary conditions is

$$\left.\begin{array}{l} u = u_0 + rx + f(y) \\ v = r(h-y) \end{array}\right\} \tag{20}$$

Here u_0 and r are constants, to be determined from measurements on the glacier, and $f(y)$ is a function of y. This function is determined by the stresses, as we shall see (equation 25). We take $f(0) = 0$ so that u_0 is the velocity at the origin. The value of r is the longitudinal strain rate $\partial u/\partial x$ measured at the surface. The solution implies that $\partial u/\partial x$ does not vary with depth y. The solution also shows that v has the same sign as r.

The stresses are determined from the equilibrium equations. These express the fact that, in the absence of accelerations, the forces applied to the surface of a body must balance the "body forces", such as gravity, which act on all parts of the body. The equations are derived by considering the equilibrium of a small cube with sides parallel to the coordinate axes. (See for example Jaeger, 1962, pp. 115–18.) In the present case of flow confined to the xy plane, the equations are

$$\partial\sigma_x/\partial x + \partial\tau_{xy}/\partial y = -\varrho g \sin\alpha \tag{21}$$

$$\partial\tau_{xy}/\partial x + \partial\sigma_y/\partial y = -\varrho g \cos\alpha \tag{22}$$

By our simplifying assumption that stresses are independent of x, the first term in each equation is zero. Boundary conditions are that, on the surface, τ_{xy} is zero and σ_y is $-P$, the atmospheric pressure. The minus sign denotes compression. The solutions are

$$\left.\begin{array}{l} \tau_{xy} = -\varrho g y \sin\alpha \\ \sigma_y = -P - \varrho g y \cos\alpha \end{array}\right\} \tag{23}$$

Substitution of these values in (15) gives

$$\sigma_x = -P - \varrho g y \cos \alpha \pm 2[\tau^2 - (\varrho g y \sin \alpha)^2]^{1/2} \qquad (24)$$

Equation (24) is the solution for σ_x, but to complete it we have to show how to determine τ. We also have to determine $f(y)$ in (20) to complete the velocity solution. From (20)

$$\dot{\varepsilon}_{xy} = \tfrac{1}{2}\,(\partial u/\partial y + \partial v/\partial x) = \tfrac{1}{2} f'(y)$$

were the dash denotes differentiation with respect to y.

But from (18) with $n = 3$,

$$\dot{\varepsilon}_{xy} = A\tau^2 \tau_{xy}$$
$$= -A\tau^2 \varrho g y \sin \alpha \qquad \text{by (23)}$$

Thus $\qquad \partial u/\partial y = f'(y) = -2A\tau^2 \varrho g y \sin \alpha \qquad (25)$

This expression is always negative. Thus u has its greatest value at the surface, and decreases steadily with depth. Also

$$f(y) = -2A\varrho g \sin \alpha \cdot \int\limits_0^y y\tau^2 \, \mathrm{d}y$$

To determine τ, we have from (8), with $n = 3$,

$$\dot{\varepsilon}^2 = A^2 \tau^6$$

But by (16) and (20)

$$2\dot{\varepsilon}^2 = 2r^2 + \tfrac{1}{2}[f'(y)]^2$$
$$= 2r^2 + 2A^2\tau^4(\varrho g y \sin \alpha)^2$$

Thus

$$\tau^6 - \tau^4(\varrho g y \sin \alpha)^2 - (r/A)^2 = 0 \qquad (26)$$

This equation determines τ as a function of y. The stress and velocity solutions are now complete.

Now consider the stress solutions (23) and (24). The stress σ_y is equal to atmospheric pressure at the surface and becomes more negative (i.e. more compressive) linearly with depth. The shear stress τ_{xy} is zero at the surface and increases in magnitude linearly with depth. This is the same expression as obtained in the preceding section. (The sign is changed because we have reversed the direction of the y-axis.) Two solutions for σ_x are possible, corresponding to the two signs in front of the square root in (24). With the plus sign, $\sigma_x + P$ is positive at the surface and σ_x is greater than σ_y at all depths. In this case we speak of a state of *extending flow*. With the minus sign, $\sigma_x + P$ is negative at the surface and at all depths, and σ_x is always less than σ_y. In this case we speak of *compressing flow*. We shall see later what determines the type of flow at any given point in a glacier.

To express these conditions in terms of strain rates instead of stresses, we note that by definition

$$\sigma'_x = \sigma_x - \tfrac{1}{3}(\sigma_x + \sigma_y + \sigma_z)$$
$$\sigma'_z = \sigma_z - \tfrac{1}{3}(\sigma_x + \sigma_y + \sigma_z)$$

Thus
$$\sigma_x - \sigma_y = 2\sigma'_x + \sigma'_z$$
$$= A^{-1}\tau^{1-n}(2\dot{\varepsilon}_x + \dot{\varepsilon}_z) \quad \text{by (11)}$$

Since A and τ are positive, σ_x is greater or less than σ_y, that is, flow is extending or compressing, according as $2\dot{\varepsilon}_x + \dot{\varepsilon}_z$ is positive or negative. This is the general condition. On the present model, $\dot{\varepsilon}_z$ is zero and $\dot{\varepsilon}_x = r$. In this case, flow is extending or compressing according as r (the longitudinal strain rate at the surface) is positive or negative. Laminar flow is the special case of $r = 0$. In this case $\tau = \varrho g y \sin \alpha$ by (26) and the velocity solution (20) reduces to the solution (14), obtained previously.

To summarize the important results of this analysis.

1. Two states of flow are possible: Extending flow: $\sigma_x > \sigma_y$, σ_x tensile in the upper layers. Compressing flow: $\sigma_x < \sigma_y$, σ_x compressive at all depths.

2. On the present model, these conditions are equivalent to: Extending flow: $r > 0$. Compressing flow: $r < 0$.

3. The velocity component u has its greatest value at the surface and decreases steadily with depth.

4. The velocity component v varies linearly with depth. It is

downwards or upwards relative to the surface according as r is positive or negative.

5. The longitudinal strain rate does not change with depth.

The formulae for stresses and velocities are exact under the assumptions stated at the beginning: no approximations were made in the mathematics. How well the results apply in an actual glacier thus depends on how realistic the assumptions are in any particular case. Let us examine these assumptions.

The slab of ice was assumed to be infinitely wide. This may be a reasonable assumption for an ice sheet. It is not valid for a typical valley glacier. The modifications to the theory which are needed to cover this case are discussed in a subsequent section. They do not change any of the five conclusions listed above.

Another assumption was that upper and lower surfaces had the same slope. This is not true at most places in a glacier. Let α_s, α_b be the slopes of the upper surface and the base, relative to horizontal. We still take the x-axis in the surface. We showed previously that the surface slope had to be used in calculation of the shear stress. The main modification occurs in the boundary condition at the base, used in the solution for v. The condition that the velocity component perpendicular to the base must be zero now gives

$$-u_b \sin (\alpha_b - \alpha_s) + v_b \cos (\alpha_b - \alpha_s) = 0 \qquad (27)$$

where suffix b denotes values at the base. If $\alpha_b - \alpha_s$ is small this reduces to

$$v_b = u_b(\alpha_b - \alpha_s)$$

This condition is met if the previous solution for v (equation 20) is changed to

$$v = r(h-y) + u_b(\alpha_b - \alpha_s)$$

With this modification, the stress and velocity solutions should remain good approximations, at places in the glacier where the difference between α_b and α_s is small. In the present context we mean by "slope" the average slope measured over a distance comparable with the ice thickness.

In a real glacier, thickness, slope and other features vary with distance x, contrary to an assumption in the theory. However, the solutions should be reasonable approximations at places in the glacier where thickness and slope do not change much in a distance comparable with the thickness (i.e. at places where $\partial h/\partial x$, $\partial^2 h/\partial x^2$ and higher derivatives are small). The predicted variations with y will probably be better approximations than any predicted variation with x. For example, equations (20) imply that u varies linearly with x and that v does not depend on x. These are at best approximations over short distances. See for example Fig. 5.3 (page 74). In a later section we relax the assumption that stresses do not vary with x.

One further feature of these solutions must be pointed out. On perfect plasticity theory, the thickness of the glacier is determined at each point. It is the thickness for which the shear stress is equal to the yield stress (1 bar approximately). In the present theory, the solutions have to be cut off arbitrarily at whatever value of y corresponds to the actual ice thickness. No boundary condition at the lower surface was set in the stress solutions or in the solution for u. The velocity at the base is in fact determined by the characteristics of the glacier bed as well as by the properties of ice, and this velocity varies from place to place. Chapter 7 deals with this subject. However, our knowledge of processes at the glacier bed, of what determines the velocity of sliding and how it is related to the shear stress, is still inadequate. When more is known about this aspect of glacier flow, improvements to the present theory should be possible.

Tests of Theoretical Predictions

Let us now see how the results of the preceding analysis compare with field observations. Borehole measurements have confirmed that in general velocity u decreases with increasing depth (Gerrard and others, 1952; Sharp, 1953; Mathews, 1959), although small discrepancies have been observed in the upper parts of a few boreholes (Sharp, 1960, p. 40; Savage and Paterson, 1963). The statement that the component v is downwards relative to the surface at places where the longitudinal strain rate is positive, and upwards when strain rate is negative, is broadly true.

See Fig. 5.3 and 5.4 (pages 74, 75) for illustrations of these results. The value of v at depth cannot be determined from measurements in a borehole. Thus there are no data to show whether or not a linear variation of v with depth is a good approximation.

Savage and Paterson (1963) have tested whether longitudinal strain rate varies with depth on Athabasca Glacier. Measurements were made on the centreline of the glacier in an area where ice thickness, glacier width, and slopes of surface and bed change only slowly with x, and where surface and bed slopes differ by only a few degrees. Apart from the fact that the width of the glacier is finite, which should not affect the particular result under discussion, the restrictions on the theory should be met. The method was as follows.

Measurements showed that the transverse strain rate was small compared with the longitudinal one. In this case, the condition of incompressibility is

$$\partial u/\partial x = -\partial v/\partial y \qquad (17)$$

Hence, for constant x and z

$$\int_0^h (\partial u/\partial x)\, \mathrm{d}y = -\int_0^h (\partial v/\partial y)\, \mathrm{d}y = v_s - v_b$$

where suffixes s and b denote values at surface and bed and h is ice thickness. The left-hand side can be written $h\bar{\dot{\varepsilon}}_x$ where $\bar{\dot{\varepsilon}}_x$ is the longitudinal strain rate averaged over the thickness at the point. Also, at the bed, the velocity component perpendicular to the bed must be zero. This gives, as in (27),

$$v_b = u_b \tan (\alpha_b - \alpha_s)$$

Thus

$$\bar{\dot{\varepsilon}}_x = [v_s - u_b \tan (\alpha_b - \alpha_s)]/h \qquad (28)$$

Of the quantities on the right-hand side of (28), α_s and v_s were measured, h and α_b were determined by seismic measurements, and u_b was measured in boreholes. Thus the value of $\bar{\dot{\varepsilon}}_x$ was calculated for comparison with the value of $\dot{\varepsilon}_x$ measured at the surface. The two should of course be equal if $\dot{\varepsilon}_x$ does not vary with depth. A less precise test can be carried out at points where there are no boreholes, by calculating limiting values of $\bar{\dot{\varepsilon}}_x$ corresponding to the limiting values of u_b, namely 0 and u_s. Note that this method of calculating $\bar{\dot{\varepsilon}}_x$ is not restricted to any particular flow law, or to a glacier in a steady state ($\partial h/\partial t = 0$ in a steady state).

Differences between mean and surface values of $\dot{\varepsilon}_x$ were larger than could reasonably be attributed to experimental errors. It was concluded that $\dot{\varepsilon}_x$ was not constant with depth in this part of Athabasca Glacier. The theoretical result that $\dot{\varepsilon}_x$ should be constant with depth is a consequence of the assumption that the thickness of the model glacier is constant. If one allows a slow variation of thickness with x, a velocity solution more general than (20), in which $\dot{\varepsilon}_x$ does vary with y, may be obtained.

Determination of Longitudinal Strain Rate

In the theoretical model, the longitudinal strain rate at the surface, denoted by r, was regarded as a constant. Its value in any particular case was to be found by measurements on the glacier. The analysis showed that the basic equations have a solution in which r is not zero. It did not show what in fact determines r. We saw in Chapter 5 that r is largely determined by the mass balance. We now consider this question further.

Take the x-axis horizontal, positive in the direction of flow, and the y-axis vertical, positive upwards. The y coordinates of the glacier surface and bed are denoted by h_s and h_b; these are arbitrary functions of x.

In an infinitely wide glacier, or on the centreline of one in which the width is finite but constant, the condition that the mass of an element of ice remains constant is

$$\partial q/\partial x + \partial h/\partial t = b$$

Here b is the net mass balance (expressed as thickness of ice and measured vertically), $h = h_s - h_b$, and q, the discharge, is given by

$$q = \int_{h_b}^{h_s} u \, dy$$

It follows that

$$\partial q/\partial x = u_s h'_s - u_b h'_b + hr$$

where r is the longitudinal strain rate, averaged over the glacier thickness. (If we assume that this strain rate does not change with depth, r is the surface value.) Also

$$h'_s = dh_s/dx = -\tan \alpha_s$$
$$h'_b = dh_b/dx = -\tan \alpha_b$$

Thus

$$r = h^{-1}(b + u_s \tan \alpha_s - u_b \tan \alpha_b - \partial h/\partial t)$$

At most places in a glacier, the first term on the right-hand side is the most important. This gives the result, quoted previously, that r is positive if b is positive (accumulation area) and negative if b is negative (ablation area). The equation also shows the other factors on which r depends. Nye (1959b) has shown that the result can be extended to the case when the glacier's width varies with distance x by inserting a term $-\bar{u}Z^{-1}(\partial Z/\partial x)$ on the right-hand side. Here Z is the width of the glacier and $\bar{u}$ is the velocity averaged over a cross-section. Thus r will tend to be positive at places where the glacier becomes narrower in the down-glacier direction. (For the discharge to remain constant, the velocity will have to increase as the cross-section decreases.)

Variations of Longitudinal Stress along the Glacier

In previous analyses, we assumed that the longitudinal stress σ_x and the shear stress τ_{xy} did not vary with x, the distance along the glacier. Collins (1968) has considered the effect of variations of σ_x with x.

We consider two-dimensional flow, as before. We use a coordinate system fixed in space, with x-axis horizontal, as in the preceding section. This is the most convenient system for considering variations with x. As before, the y coordinates of the surface and bed are h_s and h_b, arbitrary functions of x (see Fig. 6.4). The equilibrium equations for the stresses are then

$$\partial\sigma_x/\partial x + \partial\tau_{xy}/\partial y = 0 \qquad (29)$$

$$\partial\tau_{xy}/\partial x + \partial\sigma_y/\partial y = \varrho g \qquad (30)$$

Boundary conditions are that, at the surface, the stress perpendicular to the surface and the shear stress are both zero. These two stresses can be expressed in terms of σ_x, σ_y and τ_{xy}. Equating to zero leads to the conditions

$$\left.\begin{array}{l} (\sigma_x)_s = (\tau_{xy})_s/h_s' \\ (\sigma_y)_s = (\tau_{xy})_s h_s' \end{array}\right\} \tag{31}$$

An integrated form of one of the stress equilibrium equations can be obtained by considering the equilibrium of the region

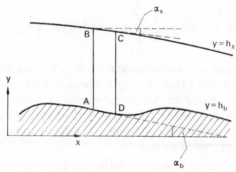

FIG. 6.4. Coordinate system for glacier of arbitrary shape.

$ABCD$ in Fig. 6.4. Balance of components parallel to the bed gives

$$\tau_b \sec \alpha_b - \varrho g h \sin \alpha_b = \cos \alpha_b \cdot \frac{\partial}{\partial x} \int_{h_b}^{h_s} \sigma_x \, \mathrm{d}y - \sin \alpha_b \cdot \frac{\partial}{\partial x} \int_{h_b}^{h_s} \tau_{xy} \, \mathrm{d}y \tag{32}$$

Here $h = h_s - h_b$ and τ_b is the value of τ_{xy} on the bed. Now

$$\frac{\partial}{\partial x} \int_{h_b}^{h_s} \tau_{xy} \, \mathrm{d}y = h_s'(\tau_{xy})_s - h_b'\tau_b + \int_{h_b}^{h_s} (\partial \tau_{xy}/\partial x) \, \mathrm{d}y$$

$$= h_s'(\tau_{xy})_s - h_b'\tau_b + \varrho g h - (\sigma_y)_s + (\sigma_y)_b \quad \text{by} \quad (30)$$

Two terms on the right-hand side cancel, by (31). Thus (32)

becomes

$$\tau_b \sec\alpha_b - \varrho gh\sin\alpha_b = \cos\alpha_b \cdot \frac{\partial}{\partial x}\int_{h_b}^{h_s}\sigma_x\,\mathrm{d}y - \sin\alpha_b\cdot[\varrho gh + (\sigma_y)_b - h_b'\tau_b]$$

Now assume that α_s, α_b are small. Thus, for example,

$$\sin\alpha_b = \alpha_b = -h_b'$$

and $h_b'^2$ can be neglected compared with 1. The last equation reduces to

$$\tau_b + \varrho ghh_b' = \frac{\partial}{\partial x}\int_{h_b}^{h_s}\sigma_x\,\mathrm{d}y + h_b'[\varrho gh + (\sigma_y)_b] \qquad (33)$$

We now make a second assumption: $\partial\tau_{xy}/\partial x$ is negligible compared with $\partial\sigma_y/\partial y$. (This assumption was also made in the previous analysis. However, we also assumed then that $\partial\sigma_x/\partial x$ was negligible. We don't do this now.) With this assumption and since h_s' is small, the boundary condition (31) reduces to $(\sigma_y)_s = 0$, and (30) can be integrated to give

$$\left.\begin{array}{l}\sigma_y = -\varrho g(h_s - y) \\ (\sigma_y)_b = -\varrho gh\end{array}\right\} \qquad (34)$$

It follows that the last term in (33) is zero.

We have seen that, because ice is incompressible, strain rates are related to the stress deviators, not the stresses. Thus we wish to express the right-hand side of (33) in terms of $\sigma_x - \sigma_y$ instead of σ_x. This can be done because by (34),

$$\frac{\partial}{\partial x}\int_{h_b}^{h_s}\sigma_y\,\mathrm{d}y = -\frac{\partial}{\partial x}\left(\frac{1}{2}\varrho gh^2\right) = -\varrho ghh'$$

equation (33) can thus be written

$$\tau_b + \varrho ghh_b' = \frac{\partial}{\partial x}\int_{h_b}^{h_s}(\sigma_x - \sigma_y)\,\mathrm{d}y - \varrho ghh'$$

or

$$\tau_b - \varrho gh\alpha_s = \frac{\partial}{\partial x}\int_{h_b}^{h_s}(\sigma_x - \sigma_y)\,\mathrm{d}y = \partial F/\partial x \qquad (35)$$

Here F, the "longitudinal force", equals $h(\bar{\sigma}_x - \bar{\sigma}_y)$, where bars denote average values over the glacier thickness.

In his analysis, Collins first deduced a general relation involving the stress deviators and then made the two simplifying assumptions. The algebra is somewhat complex, so the reader is referred to the original paper for details. Previous to Collins's work, Orowan (1949) had pointed out the importance of the longitudinal force and Lliboutry (1958a) had used equation (35) in the analysis of data from the Mer de Glace. Neither of these authors derived the equation rigorously however.

In equation (35), the term $\partial F/\partial x$ can be regarded as a correction term to the usual formula (12) for calculating τ_b. The correction arises when one considers variations of longitudinal stress with distance x. To evaluate the term, we need to know the value of the stress deviator $\frac{1}{2}(\sigma_x - \sigma_y)$. This can be calculated from measured strain rates by using the flow law. We shall discuss this further in Chapter 9 when we examine how the surface slope of an ice sheet is related to the topography of its bed.

Effect of Sides of Valley

So far we have assumed that the length and width of the model glacier were much greater than its thickness. This is reasonable as regards a glacier's length, but not for its width. The width of most valley glaciers is only three or four times their thickness. The next step is to see how this fact modifies the stresses and velocities. The following analysis is due to Nye (1965a).

The model is as follows. Ice flows down a long channel of uniform slope α and uniform cross-section. The upper surface is a plane, also of slope α. We take x-axis on the centreline, positive in the direction of flow, y-axis normal to the surface, positive downwards. The z-axis thus runs across the glacier. It is assumed that u, the x component, is the only non-zero velocity component. We are interested in how u varies with depth and with distance across the glacier. So we assume that u is a function of y and z but not of x. These assumptions imply that $\dot{\varepsilon}_x$, $\dot{\varepsilon}_y$, $\dot{\varepsilon}_z$, $\dot{\varepsilon}_{yz}$ are all zero. It then follows from (11) that σ'_x, σ'_y, σ'_z, τ_{yz} are all zero, and thus that

$$\sigma_x = \sigma_y = \sigma_z$$

and, by (7), $$\tau^2 = \tau_{xy}^2 + \tau_{zx}^2 \tag{36}$$

The equilibrium equations for the stresses reduce to

$$\partial\tau_{xy}/\partial y + \partial\tau_{zx}/\partial z = -\varrho g \sin\alpha \tag{37}$$

$$\partial\sigma_y/\partial y = -\varrho g \cos\alpha \tag{38}$$

Equations (11) show that

$$\partial u/\partial y = 2A\tau^{n-1}\tau_{xy} \tag{39}$$

$$\partial u/\partial z = 2A\tau^{n-1}\tau_{zx} \tag{40}$$

By (38) $$\sigma_x = \sigma_y = \sigma_z = -\varrho g y \cos\alpha - P$$

where P is atmospheric pressure. Equations (37), (39) and (40) are sufficient to determine τ_{xy}, τ_{zx} and u. Boundary conditions are that τ_{xy} is zero on the upper surface and that u is zero on the lower surface. The second condition implies that the glacier does not slip on its bed.

These equations can be solved analytically when the cross-section of the channel is a semi-circle. Nye used a computer to obtain numerical solutions for the cases when the channel cross-section is a rectangle, half of an ellipse, and a parabola. Of these, a parabola is probably the best approximation to an actual glacial valley. (The other shapes imply that the valley walls are vertical at the glacier surface.) We shall therefore quote some of Nye's results for a parabolic cross-section. An index $n = 3$ in the flow law was used in all calculations.

1. On the centreline, near the surface

$$\tau_{xy} = -\tfrac{1}{2}\,\varrho g y \sin\alpha \tag{41}$$

This holds for all shapes of channel, except for an infinitely-wide one when, as we saw in (23), there is no factor $\tfrac{1}{2}$.

2. On the centreline of a semi-circular channel, (41) is true not only near the surface, but at all depths. In this case τ_{xy} varies linearly with y. This is also true in an infinitely wide channel, as (23) shows. In other channels, the variation is not linear, but we can approximate τ_{xy} on the centreline by a linear function

$$\tau_{xy} = -F\varrho g y \sin\alpha \tag{42}$$

Here F is a *shape factor*. It is chosen to give the correct value of surface velocity when we integrate (39) along the y-axis. Values of F for different values of W (half the width divided by the thickness on the centreline) for different shapes of cross-section are given in Table 6.1. We see that the valley sides reduce the value of τ_{xy}. To calculate shear stresses at different depths on the centreline of a valley glacier, equation (42) with the appropriate value of F from Table 6.1 should be used. Near the surface, a factor of 0·5 can be used, as in (41). Such calculations are necessary in an analysis of borehole deformation, for example.

TABLE 6.1. "SHAPE FACTOR" F FOR CALCULATION OF SHEAR STRESS
(W = half-width/thickness on centreline)

W	F		
	parabola	semi-ellipse	rectangle
1	0·445	0·500	0·558
2	0·646	0·709	0·789
3	0·746	0·799	0·884
4	0·806	0·849	
∞	1·000	1·000	1·000

3. Figure 6.5 shows how surface velocity varies on a line across a glacier of parabolic cross-section, for different values of W. (Velocity profiles for rectangular and semi-elliptical channels are broadly similar to these.) In each case the velocity changes little across the central part of the glacier and decreases rapidly towards each side. Figure 6.6 shows a velocity profile measured by Meier (1960) across Saskatchewan Glacier. The theoretical profile, for the appropriate value of W, is shown for comparison. This profile refers to a semi-elliptical channel. Theoretical and observed curves agree closely. Also shown is the velocity profile of a highly viscous fluid in a semi-elliptical channel. This curve is a parabola. It does not fit the data well.

4. The drag of the valley walls reduces the velocity considerably.

108   THE PHYSICS OF GLACIERS

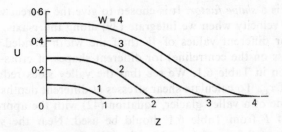

FIG. 6.5. Variation of surface velocity across a glacier in various parabolic channels. Z is the distance from the centreline divided by the ice thickness on the centreline. W is the half-width of the glacier divided by the ice thickness on the centreline. U is the ratio of the velocity in the parabolic channel to the velocity (for same ice thickness and surface slope) in a very wide channel. From Nye (1965a).

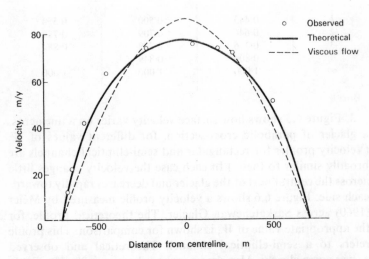

FIG. 6.6. Variation of surface velocity across Saskatchewan Glacier, Canada. Comparison of observations with the theoretical curve and with curve obtained if ice is regarded as a viscous fluid. Observations from Meier (1960).

The velocity scale in Fig. 6.5 represents the ratio of the surface velocity in the actual channel to the value the velocity would have (for the same ice thickness and surface slope) in an infinitely wide channel. For example, the velocity for $W = 2$ is about one-quarter the velocity in a very wide channel.

5. The mean velocity over a cross-section (mean over both thickness and width) is within a few per cent of the mean surface velocity (mean over width only). This result holds for values of W between 2 and 4, which includes the majority of valley glaciers. It has only been derived for a parabolic cross-section. Also, as stated earlier, this whole analysis is based on the assumption that the glacier does not slip on its bed. However, this particular result is obviously also true when sliding on the bed constitutes the whole motion of the glacier: in this case the velocity is the same at all depths. Thus the result probably holds in intermediate cases as well. This is an important practical result. Hydrologists often want to know the discharge of ice through a cross-section of a glacier. The discharge is obtained by multiplying mean velocity by area of cross-section. This result shows that the mean velocity can be obtained from a line of stakes across the glacier surface. It is not necessary to drill boreholes and measure velocity at depth.

Borehole Experiments

A borehole experiment is the best way to check how well the flow law for complex stress systems, and certain aspects of the preceding theory, apply in a real glacier.

Results of some such experiments have been analyzed in terms of equation (1), which in this case is

$$\tfrac{1}{2} \, \partial u/\partial y = A\tau_{xy}^n = A(F\varrho g y \sin \alpha_s)^n \tag{43}$$

Measurements in the borehole determine $\partial u/\partial y$ at different depths. The shear stress τ_{xy} at each depth is calculated from (42) with the appropriate value of shape factor F from Table 6.1. Values of log $\partial u/\partial y$ are plotted against log τ_{xy}. The slope and intercept of the best straight line through the points give n and $2A$. However, we have seen that (1) is only true if all stress deviators except τ_{xy} are zero. This implies that all strain rates except $\dot{\varepsilon}_{xy}$ are zero: there is no longitudinal strain rate for example. In addition, use of (43) implies that $\partial v/\partial x$ is zero. Whether these conditions are met in any particular instance can be tested by surface measurements. They will seldom be met in a real glacier. Also, in some analyses, the shape factor is omitted in calculation of shear stress. Thus it is not surprising that values of n and A derived in this way have differed from values obtained in the laboratory. A much better method is to examine the relation between the effective strain rate $\dot{\varepsilon}$ and the effective shear stress τ.

As an example of a detailed analysis, we shall use the results of Savage and Paterson (1963) from Athabasca Glacier. Data were obtained from two boreholes, some 1·5 km apart, on the centreline of the glacier in the ablation area. The boreholes, both of which penetrated to the glacier bed, were 322 and 209 m deep. In their vicinity, the glacier's thickness and width change only slowly with distance x. Slopes of surface and bed are reasonably uniform and differ from each other by only a few degrees. It is thus a favourable area for testing the theory.

Surface strain rates were measured at each borehole, by means of a diamond-shaped array of stakes as described in Chapter 5. The strain rates $\dot{\varepsilon}_z$ and $\dot{\varepsilon}_{zx}$ were an order of magnitude less than $\dot{\varepsilon}_x$. Measurements of velocity v on lines across the glacier showed that $\partial v/\partial z$ was very small near the centreline. The transverse velocity component w was also found to be very small, as expected near the centreline. Thus $\partial w/\partial y$ could be neglected. In these circumstances equation (6) reduces to

$$\dot{\varepsilon}^2 = (\partial u/\partial x)^2 + \tfrac{1}{4}(\partial u/\partial y + \partial v/\partial x)^2 \qquad (44)$$

(We have also used (5) which gives $\partial u/\partial x = -\partial v/\partial y$.)

The value of $\dot{\varepsilon}$ at each depth was determined from (44). Measurements in the borehole gave $\partial u/\partial y$ at each depth. The value of $\partial u/\partial x$ was measured at the surface. Its average value over the total thickness was calculated by the method described in an earlier section (equation 28). Its value at any depth could then be calculated, on the assumption that the variation with depth was linear. The surface value of $\partial v/\partial x$ was determined from measurements of v on a longitudinal line of stakes. As the value was small, it was considered adequate to use the same value at all depths. Approximately the top third of each borehole was excluded from the analysis, because values of $\partial u/\partial y$ there did not differ from zero by more than twice their standard errors.

Shear stresses τ_{xy} were calculated by (42), namely

$$\tau_{xy} = -F\varrho gy \sin \alpha_s$$

The value of τ was determined as follows. As one could not assume beforehand that the data fitted the power law of flow, the relation between strain rates and stress deviators was written in the general form (3)

$$\dot{\varepsilon}_{xy} = \lambda\tau_{xy}$$

where λ is a function of τ, with the corresponding relation (9)

$$\dot{\varepsilon} = \lambda\tau$$

The value of λ at each depth was found from

$$\lambda = \dot{\varepsilon}_{xy}/\tau_{xy} = \tfrac{1}{2}(\partial u/\partial y + \partial v/\partial x)(-F\varrho gy \sin \alpha_s)^{-1}$$

and then τ from

$$\tau = \dot{\varepsilon}/\lambda$$

Figure 6.7 is a graph of $\log \dot{\varepsilon}^2$ against $\log \tau^2$. Each point corresponds to one depth in one borehole over one observation period. Also shown are straight lines corresponding to the value $n = 4\cdot2$ which Glen (1955) measured in his laboratory experiments. The constant A depends on temperature. There is some indirect evidence that, in Athabasca Glacier, the ice is slightly below the pressure melting point. The two lines in Fig. 6.7 correspond to the values of A which Glen found for temperatures of 0 and $-1\cdot5°C$. (Glen in fact published two values of n, $3\cdot2$ and $4\cdot2$, with corresponding values of A. The difference arose from different ways of allowing for the initial transient part of the flow. The value $3\cdot2$ is nearer the commonly used value of 3. However the value $4\cdot2$ provides the more satisfactory fit to the data from Athabasca Glacier. This could result from the ice at depth having developed a preferred orientation; but this is pure speculation.

In any case, the difference between the two values is not very important.)

Results in the two boreholes and for the different periods are consistent with each other, and agree closely with the laboratory curves. This suggests that Nye's generalization of the flow law to complex stress systems is valid. Two features of this analysis should be noted. First, use of the shape factor F in calculating shear stress. Second, the linear variation of longitudinal strain

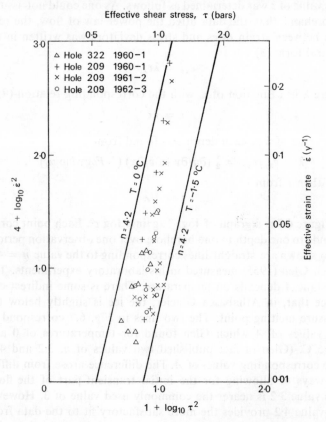

FIG. 6.7. Comparison of borehole data from Athabasca Glacier, Canada, with flow law. From Savage and Paterson (1965).

rate with depth, which is not included in any of the preceding theoretical models. These features had to be included to obtain reasonable agreement with the laboratory results. As F is about 0·6 and n is 4·2, omission of F would increase the calculated strain rate at any given depth by a factor of about 8. Moreover, when the surface value of $\dot{\varepsilon}_x$ was used at all depths, the strain rate appeared to decrease with increasing stress in the upper part of the stress range. This can be taken as evidence, additional to that quoted in an earlier section, that $\dot{\varepsilon}_x$ does vary with depth.

In general, however, the satisfactory agreement between the field and laboratory results gives us considerable confidence in applying results of Nye's theoretical work to conditions in real glaciers.

Crevasses

The way in which crevasses form illustrates some of the previous theoretical results.

We return to the model of a parallel-sided slab of ice resting on an inclined rough plane; the length and width of the slab are large compared with its thickness. The origin is taken on the surface; the x-axis lies in the surface pointing down slope; the y-axis is perpendicular to the surface, positive downwards; the z-axis runs across the slope. We saw that, in this model, τ_{zx}, τ_{yz} and σ'_z are zero. Moreover, at the surface, τ_{xy} is zero. We also saw that the solutions for τ_{xy} and the velocities, obtained for this model, have to be modified before they are applicable to a valley glacier. However, we shall not use these particular solutions. The following discussion of crevasse depths therefore applies near the centreline of a valley glacier, and in an ice sheet.

We saw that two types of flow are possible. In extending flow, σ_x is tensile in the upper layers. If this stress exceeds the tensile strength of the ice, transverse crevasses should form. We don't expect crevasses in an area of compressing flow. We also saw that, in extending flow, although σ'_x and therefore $\dot{\varepsilon}_x$ are positive (extending) throughout the thickness, σ_x is only positive in the upper layers. Thus we might expect the depth at which σ_x reaches zero to be the maximum depth of a crevasse.

This maximum depth can be calculated (Nye, 1955). If we neglect atmospheric pressure for the moment, equation (24) shows that $\sigma_x = 0$ at depth d given by

$$(\varrho g d \cos \alpha)^2 = 4[\tau^2 - (\varrho g d \sin \alpha)^2]$$

which for small α reduces to

$$d = 2\tau/\varrho g$$

Now by (8) $\tau = (\dot\varepsilon/A)^{1/n}$

At the surface, $\dot\varepsilon_{xy}$ is zero because τ_{xy} is zero. Also, by (17), $\dot\varepsilon_x = -\dot\varepsilon_y$. Thus by (6), near the surface

$$\dot\varepsilon = \dot\varepsilon_x$$

Thus

$$d \approx 2(\dot\varepsilon_x/A)^{1/n} (\varrho g)^{-1}$$

Equation (24) shows that atmospheric pressure reduces the thickness over which σ_x is positive. However, atmospheric pressure acts within the crevasse, which will therefore continue to open until its base reaches the depth at which σ_x equals atmospheric pressure. This leads to the same value of d as before. With Glen's values of $n = 4 \cdot 2$ and $A = 0 \cdot 148$ y^{-1} $bar^{-4 \cdot 2}$ for ice at $0°C$, the last equation gives

$$d = 36\dot\varepsilon_x^{0 \cdot 24}$$

with d in metres and $\dot\varepsilon_x$ in years^{-1}. With $\dot\varepsilon_x = 0 \cdot 5$ y^{-1} this gives $d = 30$ m. This value agrees roughly with observations: measured crevasse depths in glaciers in temperate regions have seldom exceeded 25 or 30 m. A discrepancy may arise because a crevasse will modify the stress distribution in its vicinity, and thus may open up to a somewhat greater depth than predicted. Because the value of A decreases with temperature, crevasses should be deeper in arctic glaciers than in "temperate" ones. This also agrees with observation.

(A simpler method of obtaining a comparable figure for the maximum depth is to use the approximation of perfect plasticity. At the base of a vertical crevasse wall 22 m high, there is a vertical compressive stress of 2 bars plus atmospheric pressure. The horizontal stress component perpendicular to the wall is atmospheric pressure only. This stress system is equivalent to a shear stress of 1 bar on planes at 45° to the horizontal. This equals the yield stress in shear. Thus at this depth the ice will flow rapidly and fill in the crevasse. The dependence of maximum depth on temperature follows from the fact that yield stress increases with decrease of temperature.)

So far we have only considered the special stress system of our theoretical model. In a general stress system, τ_{xy} and τ_{yz} must still be zero at the surface. This implies that σ_y is one principal stress. The other principal stresses are the roots of

$$\mu^2 - (\sigma_x + \sigma_z)\,\mu + (\sigma_x\sigma_z - \tau_{xz}^2) = 0$$

Crevasses will only form at places where at least one of these two principal stresses is tensile. If only one is tensile, the crevasses should open up in the direction of that stress, that is they should run at right angles to it. This has been confirmed on Saskatchewan Glacier where Meier (1960) found that crevasses were approximately at right angles to the direction of the tensile principal strain rate.

The result can also be used to draw the patterns which crevasses should form in simple situations (Nye, 1952a). We consider a valley glacier of constant width and assume for simplicity that σ_x has the same value right across the glacier. Atmospheric pressure is neglected. The shear stress τ_{zx}, due to the drag of the valley walls, is zero on the centreline and increases towards each side.

In Fig. 6.8a, it is assumed that τ_{zx} is the only non-zero stress at the surface. In this case the principal stresses are a tensile stress of magnitude τ_{zx} and an equal compressive stress, each inclined at 45° to the coordinate axes, as shown at the top of the diagram. The crevasses will run at right angles to the tensile principal stress. They will not extend right to the centre of the glacier, because τ_{zx} is zero there.

Figure 6.8b illustrates extending flow. On the centreline, τ_{zx} is zero and the tensile principal stress is σ_x. The crevasses will run at right angles to σ_x that is, in the z direction. Near the edge the combination of σ_x and τ_{zx} is equivalent to a large tensile principal

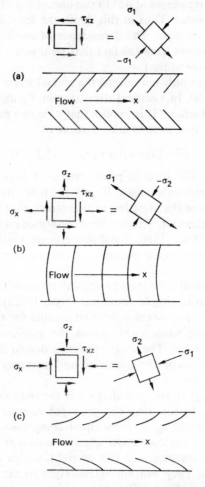

FIG. 6.8. Crevasse patterns in a valley glacier. (a) Effect of shear stress of valley walls only. (b) Shear stress and extending flow. (c) Shear stress and compressing flow. From Nye (1952a).

stress inclined at less than 45° to the x-axis, and a small compressive principal stress, as shown at the top of the diagram. The crevasses run at right angles to the tensile stress and so make an angle of more than 45° with the side of the glacier. They run in intermediate directions between the edge and the centreline.

Figure 6.8c illustrates compressing flow. Near the edge, the combination of σ_x and τ_{zx} is equivalent to a small tensile principal stress inclined at more than 45° to the x-axis, and a large compressive principal stress, as shown at the top of the diagram. The crevasses meet the sides of the glacier at less than 45°. They die out towards the centre of the glacier where τ_{zx} is zero and σ_x is compressive.

CHAPTER 7

GLACIER FLOW II: BASAL SLIDING

"Where thou perhaps...
Visitest the bottom of the monstrous world"

MILTON, *Lycidas.*

Introduction

Chapter 6 dealt with plastic deformation within a glacier. We now turn to the other component of movement, sliding of the glacier over its bed or "basal slip" as it is often called. In some cases this is the major part of the motion (see Table 5.1). Sliding is expected only in those glaciers in which the basal ice is at the pressure melting temperature. Observations by Goldthwait (1960) in a tunnel at the edge of a small ice cap in Greenland, have confirmed that, in this instance at least, a glacier frozen to its bed does not slide. Again, laboratory studies have shown that, when ice is frozen to a strong material, the interface will support tangential stresses of at least ten times the yield stress of ice.

A major obstacle to the understanding of glacier sliding is the difficulty of observing it. To do so, one has to dig a tunnel down to bedrock, a task seldom accomplished. The sliding velocity can also be calculated from measurements in a borehole, provided the hole reaches the bottom of the glacier. Another relevant fact, observed on several glaciers, is that the velocity measured at the surface increases during the melt season and, occasionally, after heavy rain. An increase in the amount of water at the glacier bed, which is supposed to have a lubricating effect, is the most plausible explanation of such increases in velocity. The mechanism of this lubrication is still obscure however. An increase in velocity during the melt season strongly suggests that a glacier is sliding on its bed.

The best developed theory of sliding is that of Weertman (1957a, 1964). This theory is widely accepted, at least in principle. Kamb and LaChapelle (1964), however, on the basis of field observations and a laboratory experiment, think that the numerical values of some of the parameters in the theory should be changed. Lliboutry (1965, pp. 647–52) has proposed a sliding mechanism additional to the two involved in Weertman's theory. This chapter deals with these topics, starting with Weertman's theory.

Basic Theory

The problem is to explain how ice, assumed to be at the pressure melting temperature, moves past bumps in the glacier bed. According to Weertman's theory, two mechanisms operate. This was originally a postulate but is now an experimental fact.

The first mechanism is pressure melting. The resistance to glacier movement must be provided by the upstream sides of bumps in the bed. There will therefore be an excess pressure on these sides. Thus ice can melt there. The melt water will flow round the bump and refreeze on the downstream side, where the pressure is lower. To maintain the process, the latent heat of fusion released on the downstream side is conducted through the obstacle and the surrounding ice to the upstream side, where it is used for melting. This mechanism does not work for large obstacles (of the order of 1 m or more in length) because the heat conducted through them is negligible. Nor will it work when the ice is below the melting point.

The second mechanism is enhanced plastic flow. All the ice is deforming plastically. However, near an obstacle, the longitudinal stress in the ice is greater than average and so the strain rate will be above average there also. Moreover, velocity is proportional to strain rate times distance. The larger the obstacle, the greater the distance over which the stress is enhanced and so the greater the velocity will be. Thus this mechanism is more effective for large obstacles than for small ones.

The glacier moves over its bed by a combination of these two processes; neither is adequate alone. We now discuss each process in detail, first treating the simplest case and then adding refinements.

The glacier bed is regarded as an inclined plane with cubical obstacles on it. Each cube has sides of length l and is separated from its neighbours by distances d, measured from the centre of each cube. We assume that a perfectly smooth ice-rock interface can support only a normal stress, not a tangential one. This is reasonable because, as the basal ice is at the melting point, there should be a thin film of water at the interface. Such a film has been observed.

We first calculate the velocity due to pressure melting. Let τ be the average shear stress which the glacier exerts on its bed. As there is one obstacle in an area d^2, the average force on each obstacle is τd^2. This force causes a compressive stress on the upstream face (area l^2) of each obstacle. It also causes a tensile stress on the downstream face, provided the ice is in contact with this face. These stresses are in addition to the hydrostatic pressure at the base of the glacier, which is much larger than τ. By symmetry, the compressive and tensile stresses are equal and so each is $\frac{1}{2}\tau d^2/l^2$. Their difference is $\tau d^2/l^2$. Because of this stress difference, the melting point of ice on the upstream side of an obstacle is lower than that on the downstream side by an amount

$$\Delta T = C\tau d^2/l^2 \tag{1}$$

where C is a numerical constant. As the ice is assumed to be at the pressure melting temperature throughout, this temperature difference exists across the obstacle.

If u_1 is the velocity due to this mechanism, a volume of ice $u_1 l^2$ is melted on the upstream face of the obstacle in unit time. This water flows round the obstacle and refreezes at the downstream face. Refreezing releases latent heat of amount $u_1 l^2 \varrho L$ in unit time, where L is latent heat of fusion and ϱ is the density of ice. This heat is conducted through the obstacle to the upstream face where it is used to melt ice. (We assume for the present that no heat is conducted through the surrounding ice.) The heat conducted in unit time is $Kl\,\Delta T$ where K is the thermal conductivity of the obstacle. It follows that

$$u_1 l^2 \varrho L = Kl\,\Delta T$$

and, by (1),

$$u_1 = (CK/L\varrho l)\,\tau R^2 \tag{2}$$

where $R = d/l$. This quantity can be regarded as a *roughness parameter* of the bed. Note that R decreases as roughness increases. Equation (2) shows that u_1 is inversely proportional to l. In other words, the pressure melting mechanism is most effective for small obstacles.

Now consider the second mechanism: increase in the rate of plastic flow around obstacles because of the additional stress they create in the adjacent ice. Let u_2 be the velocity due to this mechanism. We have already shown that the additional longitudinal stress is $\frac{1}{2}\tau R^2$. It is negative (compressive) on the upstream side of an obstacle and positive (tensile) on the downstream side. This stress will produce a strain rate proportional to $(\frac{1}{2}\tau R^2)^n$ where n is about 3 or 4 (see Chapter 6). To determine u_2 we need to know the distance x over which the excess longitudinal stress acts. A plausible assumption is that the volume of ice affected by the obstacle is about the same as the volume of the obstacle. So we take $x = l$. It follows that

$$u_2 = Al(\tfrac{1}{2}\tau R^2)^n \tag{3}$$

where A is the constant in the flow law. This velocity is directly proportional to l, the obstacle size.

So far we have assumed that all obstacles are the same size. In fact there will be a wide range of sizes. The pressure melting mechanism allows the ice to flow easily round small obstacles, while the stress enhancement mechanism does the same for large obstacles. Thus some intermediate size of obstacle will be the main hindrance to motion and so will largely determine the sliding velocity. We shall call an obstacle of this size a *controlling obstacle*. It will be of the size l_c for which u_1 and u_2 are equal. Thus, from (2) and (3)

$$(CK/L\varrho l_c)\,\tau R^2 = Al_c(\tfrac{1}{2}\tau R^2)^n$$

$$l_c = 2^{n/2}(CK/AL\varrho)^{1/2}\,\tau^{(1-n)/2}R^{1-n} \tag{4}$$

We can now derive the formula for the sliding velocity. As a first approximation, we shall assume that the sliding velocity is completely determined by the controlling obstacles. (We have already made this assumption implicitly by writing τ in (4). The shear stress in (4) should be the fraction of τ supported by the controlling obstacles.) In this case the sliding velocity u_b equals $u_1 + u_2$ and, for the controlling obstacles, $u_1 = u_2$. Therefore, from (3) and (4) or (2) and (4)

$$u_b = (KCA/L\varrho)^{1/2}\,2^{1-n/2}\tau^{(n+1)/2}R^{n+1} \tag{5}$$

The value of n is about 3 or 4. Thus the sliding velocity is proportional to about the square of the basal shear stress and the fourth power of the roughness. (Remember that a low value of R indicates a very rough bed.)

Expanded Theory

Weertman (1964) later eliminated some of the simplifying assumptions from the previous treatment. We shall only outline the changes because they merely alter the numerical factors in equation (5).

I. In the derivation of u_1, it was assumed that heat was conducted only through the obstacle. In fact, some heat will be conducted through the surrounding ice. Thermal conductivities of ice and rock are of the same order. The simplest method of allowing for this is to replace K by αK. The value of α, which will be somewhat greater than 1, might be found by a laboratory experiment.

II. In the derivation of u_2, it was assumed that the excess longitudinal stress, produced in the ice by the obstacle, was effective over a distance l equal to the obstacle size. We can generalize by replacing l by λl where λ is a constant. The distance should be of order l, so λ should be of order 1. Its value might be found by a laboratory experiment.

III. The ice was assumed to remain in contact with the downstream face of an obstacle. If this is true, the ice exerts a longitudinal tension of $\frac{1}{2}\tau R^2$ on that face, as was stated. However, if there is a cavity in the ice on the downstream side of the obstacle, there will be no longitudinal tension on the downstream face. The longitudinal compression on the upstream face will then be doubled; its value will be τR^2. The simplest way to express this is to write the longitudinal tension as $\beta\tau R^2$, with $\beta = \frac{1}{2}$ if the ice is in contact with the downstream face and $\beta = 1$ if it is not. This only affects the derivation of u_2. In the case of u_1, the important quantity is the pressure difference across the obstacle. This is τR^2 whether β is $\frac{1}{2}$ or 1.

Unless the cavity is full of water, hydrostatic pressure will tend to close it. The closure rate is proportional to $(\varrho g h)^n$ where h is the thickness of ice over the cavity, g is the acceleration due to gravity, and n is the index in the flow law. But ice flow tends to open the cavity. The rate of opening is given by (3), except that the factor $\frac{1}{2}$ must be omitted. It is proportional to $(\tau R^2)^n$. Thus cavities can form if $\tau R^2 > \varrho g h$. The value of τ is about 1 bar, which is equal to the hydrostatic pressure of about 11 m of ice. The value of R is probably in the range of 1 to 10. Thus cavities may well form in the lee of obstacles, especially where the ice is relatively thin. They have in fact been observed.

IV. The obstacles were assumed to be cubes. To generalize, let l_x, l_y, l_z be the mean dimensions of an obstacle in three orthogonal directions. The obstacle size l is then $(l_x l_y l_z)^{1/3}$. Similarly d can be interpreted as the mean spacing between the centres of obstacles.

V. The sliding velocity was assumed to be completely determined by obstacles of size l_c, the size for which the two mechanisms produce equal velocities. This assumption implies that the controlling obstacles support the whole of the basal shear stress τ. We now suppose that there are also obstacles of sizes ... $10^{-2} l_c$, $10^{-1} l_c$, $10 l_c$ .... Let τ_i be the shear stress which causes ice to flow round obstacles of size $10^i l_c$. The sum of all the τ_i must equal τ. For simplicity, Weertman assumed that the ice moved past obstacles of size less than l_c purely by pressure melting, and that increased plastic flow was solely responsible for movement round obstacles larger than l_c. With this assumption, combined with the fact that the sliding velocity must be the same for all obstacles, the value of τ_i/τ can be calculated for each i.

The result is that obstacles of size l_c support about 43 per cent of the total shear stress, another 47 per cent is supported by obstacles larger than l_c, while obstacles of size less than l_c support the remaining 10 per cent. To assume, as previously, that obstacles of size l_c support the whole shear stress is thus only a rough approximation. In equations (4) and (5), τ, the total basal shear stress, should be replaced by τ_c, the shear stress supported by the controlling obstacles. We therefore replace τ by $\gamma\tau$, where $\gamma = 0.43$, in these equations.

VI. We still assume that the roughness parameter $R (= d/l)$ is the same for obstacles of all sizes.

When all these changes are made, equations (4) and (5) become

$$l_c = (\alpha KC/L\varrho A\lambda)^{1/2}\ \beta^{-n/2}(\gamma\tau)^{(1-n)/2}R^{1-n} \qquad (4')$$

$$u_b = 2(\alpha KCA\lambda/L\varrho)^{1/2}\ \beta^{n/2}(\gamma\tau)^{(n+1)/2}R^{n+1} \qquad (5')$$

If we take n, the index in the flow law, as 3, these equations can be written as

$$l_c = A_1/\tau R^2 \qquad (4'')$$

$$u_b = A_2\tau^2 R^4 \qquad (5'')$$

where A_1, A_2 are constants.

In Chapter 6, we showed that, for "laminar flow", the velocity due to differential movement within the ice was also proportional to a power of the basal shear stress. Thus, in theoretical analyses, both cases can be included in a relation of the form

$$u = \text{constant} \times \tau^m$$

For plastic deformation, m is about 4; for basal slip, about 2. The constants are also different for the two cases.

Substitution of numerical values into equation (5') gives values of sliding velocity of the correct order of magnitude. Close agreement between theory and observation can hardly be expected in view of the simplifying assumptions made in the theory and the somewhat unrealistic model taken for the glacier bed. Another difficulty is that the velocity is very sensitive to the value of the roughness R and this quantity is very difficult to measure. Again, the assumption that R is the same for all sizes of obstacles is unlikely to be correct.

Weertman (1964) has published graphs of sliding velocity and controlling obstacle size against shear stress, for different values of roughness parameter. These are useful for showing the relationships between these quantities. Numerical predictions based on these graphs may be unreliable however because of the values Weertman takes for two of the constants in equations (4') and (5'). For A, the constant in Glen's flow law, Weertman uses the value 0.017 bar^{-3} y^{-1}. In fact, this value applies when $n = 4 \cdot 2$ and the ice is at a temperature of $-1 \cdot 5°C$. As Weertman takes $n = 3$ and the ice is assumed to be at the melting point, it would be better to use Glen's value for $n = 3 \cdot 2$ and ice at $0°C$, namely $0 \cdot 854$ bar$^{-3 \cdot 2}$ y^{-1}. Again, the constant C in equations (1), (4') and (5') relates the change in melting temperature to the change in pressure which produces it. For a hydrostatic pressure C has the value $-0 \cdot 0074$ deg bar^{-1} given by the Clausius–Clapeyron equation. However, the stress difference across an obstacle at the glacier bed is a uniaxial stress. What value to take for C in this case is somewhat uncertain (Weertman, 1964; Lliboutry, 1964, pp. 35–36), although the consensus of opinion appears to be that the same value should be used.

Effect of Water at the Glacier Bed

Weertman (1964) also considered how a layer of water at the glacier bed might change the sliding velocity. Such a layer would submerge the smaller obstacles and so they would not support any of the basal shear stress. Obstacles thicker than the water layer would have to support greater stresses than normal, and so plastic flow, and the sliding velocity, would be increased. Weertman calculated that a water layer with a thickness of about $\frac{1}{10}$ of the controlling obstacle size could increase the sliding velocity by 20 per cent. Weertman, using plausible numerical values in equation (4'), also calculated that the controlling obstacle size is probably in the range 0·5 to 10 cm. Thus a water layer only a few millimetres thick might change the sliding velocity appreciably. This is a possible mechanism of the "lubrication" postulated to account for observed increases of glacier velocity during the melt season and after heavy rain. Weertman has also suggested that a glacier surge may occur when the thickness of the water layer exceeds the controlling obstacle size (see Chapter 8).

Whether such a water layer can exist is a controversial question. A normal geothermal heat flux will melt about 6 mm of ice in a year. The heat produced by sliding may melt about the same amount. This water must flow away, but it will form a layer too thin to have any effect on the sliding velocity. It is uncertain whether an appreciable quantity of the surface water which penetrates to the glacier bed can flow as a layer rather than in channels. The water is certainly in channels when it emerges from under the terminus. Further up the glacier, however, where the ice is much thicker than at the terminus, the hydrostatic pressure of the ice may largely control the flow of water at the bed. This flow will then depend on the slope of the glacier surface rather than on the topography of the bed, and in this case the water might flow as a layer.

Another possibility is that the water at the bed may be contained in cavities, rather than forming a continuous layer. Lliboutry (1965, pp. 647–52) thinks that water-filled cavities play an important part in the sliding process. In the previous discussion of the formation of cavities behind obstacles, we assumed that the cavities were empty. But if this were so, the pressure of ice against bedrock at the margin of the cavity would be less than the pressure some distance away from the cavity. Any water would flow down the pressure gradient into the cavity. Cavities will enlarge as long as there is enough water to fill them, and water in one cavity may partly submerge obstacles downstream from it. The more water there is, the smaller will be the area of contact between ice and rock, and so the faster will the glacier slide. Moreover, ice flow will enlarge the cavities as the velocity increases and this will further decrease the area of contact. Thus Lliboutry believes that the friction between ice and bedrock decreases as velocity increases and that water-filled cavities must exist at places where the sliding velocity is high (of the order of 100 m y^{-1}).

In his theory of sliding, Lliboutry (1965, pp. 640–52) considers, in addition to the two sliding mechanisms proposed by Weertman, the effect of water-filled cavities. The water pressure in the cavities is regarded as an independent variable. This is not unreasonable, but the value of this pressure can only be guessed. Thus, as Weertman (1967) has pointed out, Lliboutry's theory, in its present form, can hardly be used to predict numerical values of sliding velocity.

Weertman and Lliboutry also use different models for the glacier bed. On Weertman's model, as we have seen, the glacier bed is rough in both horizontal directions. Lliboutry, on the other hand, adopts a "washboard" model in which the glacier bed is rough in the direction of flow but smooth in the cross-glacier direction.

In all such discussions of how water might change the sliding velocity, the glacier bed is assumed to be impermeable to water. This is a very dubious assumption. Many rocks are permeable. Also, as sliding only occurs when the basal ice is at the pressure melting point, glaciers which slide will not be underlain by permafrost. Again, the permeability may depend on the amount of water present. This is just one aspect of the problem of glacier sliding which needs further investigation.

Observations

We now turn to field observations and discuss the extent to which they support the foregoing theoretical ideas. To date, the most detailed investigation is that of Kamb and LaChapelle (1964) in a tunnel in Blue Glacier, U.S.A. Previous to this, Carol (1947) had observed basal slip at the bottom of deep marginal crevasses, and Haefeli (1951) and McCall (1952) had done so in tunnels. Such tunnels are usually cut horizontally from the surface, at places where the glacier is steep and thin.

McCall's tunnel was in a small corrie glacier in Norway. The tunnel was about 100 m long, the ice was 50 m thick, and the measured sliding velocity was 2 m y^{-1}. McCall noted that the layer of ice in contact with bedrock differed from the rest of the ice. This layer, approximately 30 cm thick, contained dirt and was more or less free of air bubbles. McCall thought it had been formed by refreezing of meltwater which had trickled down from the bergschrund at the head of the glacier. Alternatively, it might have resulted from pressure melting and refreezing as the glacier moved over its bed. McCall also observed small cavities on the downstream side of bumps.

Kamb and LaChapelle's tunnel was near the side of Blue Glacier and near the top of an icefall. The point where bedrock was reached was a vertical distance of 26 m below the surface. The surface slope was 28°; the bed slope was 22° and increased to 55° a short distance further down the icefall. The basal shear stress was 0·7 bar. As the ice was thin, the hydrostatic pressure was low and comparable with the basal shear stress.

Kamb and LaChapelle made the following observations.

1. Differential motion in the lowest layers of ice was measured by a vertical line of pegs spaced 10 cm apart. The lowest peg, 10 cm above bedrock, moved 1·6 cm day^{-1}. This movement represents slipping of the ice over bedrock. The highest peg, 150 cm above bedrock, moved 1·8 cm day^{-1}. Most of the differential movement occurred in the lowest 50 cm of ice. The velocity at the glacier surface was equal in magnitude and direction to the velocity at 150 cm above the bed.

2. There was a thin layer of water, at the pressure melting point, at the ice-rock interface. Its existence was inferred from the fact that the basal ice froze to the rock when the pressure was released by cutting out the ice immediately above.

3. The basal ice layer differed in several respects from the ice above. The basal layer had smaller grains and contained much more dirt. The layer was relatively free of bubbles but, in its upper part, contained chains of bubbles aligned in the direction of flow. The thickness of the layer varied from almost zero on the tops of bumps in the bedrock to up to 3 cm elsewhere. The

upper boundary of the layer, which was quite distinct, appeared as a straight line in sections cut parallel to the direction of flow, and coincided with the crest of the first bump upstream. This basal ice was identified as a *regelation layer* that is, ice formed by the refreezing, on the downstream side of an obstacle, of water melted on the upstream side.

4. The ice bridged hollows in the bedrock. This was observed for hollows whose lengths ranged from 4 cm to 10 m. Separation between ice and rock varied from 1 to 20 cm. A hollow was bridged provided there was no corresponding bump upstream from it. Thus these bridged hollows were not the same as cavities formed on the downstream side of obstacles. However, the ice was separated from bedrock over a distance of 10 m down glacier from the tunnel. As the tunnel reached bedrock near the crest of a large rise, this separation over 10 m could be described as a large cavity in the lee of the rise. Large cavities would be expected because the hydrostatic pressure is low. Neither the bedrock hollows nor the cavity contained water.

5. The ice in the regelation layer appeared to be undeformed by flow. However, there were foliation planes in the ice at distances of 50 cm and more above the bed. These planes, and the regelation layer as a whole, were bent downwards in the downstream direction, corresponding to the steepening of the glacier bed.

These observations show the existence of both pressure melting and plastic deformation. As the pressure melting mechanism is unimportant at obstacles larger than the controlling obstacle size, l_c, the maximum thickness of the regelation layer (3 cm) may be taken as a measure of l_c. This is the same order of magnitude as the values of l_c which Weertman calculated from equation (4′). On the other hand, Kamb and LaChapelle noted that the regelation layer was deformed over horizontal distances of the order of 50 cm, but not over smaller distances. Deformation is expected over distances comparable with l_c, because plastic deformation is important for obstacles of this size, but not for smaller ones. Kamb and LaChapelle therefore concluded that only the pressure melting mechanism was effective at obstacles a few centimetres in size, and that the controlling obstacle size was really about 50 cm. Thus these authors think that Weertman's theory overemphasizes the role of enhanced plastic flow in the sliding process.

One should remember that conditions at the tunnel (low basal shear stress, low hydrostatic pressure, steep surface and bed, low velocity consisting almost entirely of basal slip) were not typical of conditions at most places in a valley glacier. Similar observations should be made in other glaciers.

Kamb and LaChapelle (1964) also performed a laboratory experiment to study the problem. A small cube of solid material, with a wire attached, was frozen into a block of ice. The other end of the wire was brought out of the bottom of the block and a weight was hung on it. The ice, initially at $-30°C$, was allowed to warm up. The motion of the cube through the ice was measured. Results, for cubes of three different materials, are shown in Fig. 7.1. The velocity of the cube increased in the later stages of the experiment. No observations were made between 8 and 22 hr, but extrapolation of the two segments of the curve suggests that the velocity increased at about 15 hr. The interpretation is

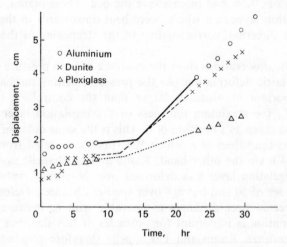

FIG. 7.1. Results of experiment of Kamb and LaChapelle (1964).

that, for the first 15 hr, the cube moved as a result of plastic deformation of the surrounding ice. (Flow was also relatively rapid in the first two or three hours: this is the initial transient stage observed by Glen and others.) At 15 hr, the ice at the base of the cube is presumed to have reached the pressure melting temperature. Thereafter, the pressure melting mechanism contributed to the movement of the cube through the ice.

Examination of the ice through which the cube had passed revealed some features similar to those of the regelation layer at the glacier bed. On the other hand, the structure of the ice surrounding the cube was essentially unchanged. Kamb and LaChapelle regard this as further evidence that Weertman's theory overrates the contribution of plastic flow.

To sum up. Most glaciologists agree that the two mechanisms suggested by Weertman contribute to basal sliding: their relative importance is in dispute. Further field observations are needed to resolve this problem. Little is known about whether water-filled cavities have an important influence at high sliding rates, as Lliboutry asserts. Field measurements have so far been made only at places where the sliding velocity is less than 10 m y^{-1}. Basal slip, and the related topic of the cause of glacier surges, are perhaps the most important unsolved problems in glacier dynamics today.

Water in a Temperate Glacier

To complement the earlier discussion of water at the glacier bed, we shall now summarize what is known about the distribution of water within a glacier which is at or near the pressure melting temperature.

Flow records of glacier-fed rivers provide some information on this subject. Such data have been studied by Meier and Tangborn (1961) (South Cascade Glacier, U.S.A.), Mathews (1963) (Athabasca Glacier, Canada) and Elliston (unpublished) (Gorner Glacier, Switzerland), among others. During fine summer weather, the discharge (volume flowing in unit time) of a glacial stream shows a marked diurnal variation. The maximum instantaneous discharge may be roughly twice the minimum. The daily peak in discharge usually occurs around 1700 or 1800 hours, that is, a few hours after the daily peak in the rate of ice melt. Total daily discharge is usually greatest in late July or early August. Some water continues to flow throughout the winter; the amount appears to be of the same order of magnitude as the amount of water which an average value of geothermal heat flux would melt from the base of the glacier.

One question is: How long does water take to travel through and underneath the glacier? The travel time is sometimes assumed to be a few hours, merely because this is the time difference between the daily peaks in discharge and rate of melt. But there is not much evidence that the water flowing past the gauge on a particular day was produced by melting that same day, rather than say a few days earlier. One test is to throw dye into a moulin and watch for its reappearance from under the terminus. Results of such experiments have been inconclusive. In some cases the dye has reappeared within an hour; in others it has never been seen again. In any case, the behaviour of water flowing down moulins is not necessarily typical of conditions in the glacier as a whole, especially the moulins near the terminus that have usually been chosen for such experiments. If the mean travel time of water is only a few hours, discharges measured during the night, when there is very little melting, are surprisingly high.

An interesting feature of the streamflow records from Athabasca Glacier, studied by Mathews, was the occurrence of "floods". These interrupted the normal diurnal cycle and were apparently unrelated to weather conditions. In some cases, discharge took one or two days to attain a maximum and remained above average for up to a week. Short irregular surges of water occurred quite frequently during any one flood. Records covering thirteen summers showed at least ten floods of 250,000 m³ or more, and numerous smaller ones. There are no ice-dammed lakes around Athabasca Glacier so the water must have been stored within the ice. Drainage of a single chamber of the size of the larger floods would certainly have caused some surface subsidence; but none was seen. The water must therefore have been contained in a number of smaller cavities.

There is other evidence that water-filled cavities exist in glaciers. Haefeli and Brentani (1955) have reported that several were encountered during construction of a tunnel through the small icecap at the Jungfraujoch in Switzerland. Fisher (1963) has described a water-filled cavity, estimated to be at least 1000 m³ in volume, encountered while tunnelling in ice on the Breithorn in the Swiss Alps. These cavities were 20 to 30 m below the surface. Both these tunnels were in ice which was a few degrees below the melting point. Savage and Paterson (1963), while drilling in Athabasca Glacier, noticed that the drill would occasionally fall freely, sometimes for as much as 1 m. This happened even at depths greater than 200 m. The drill was presumed to have penetrated a water-filled cavity.

Glen (1954) has suggested a mechanism by which water can penetrate a glacier. Consider a vertical hole, full of water. The normal stress on the wall of the hole, at depth h below the surface, is equal to the hydrostatic pressure of the water there. This is $\varrho_\omega g h$ where ϱ_ω is the density of water, and g the acceleration due to gravity. The vertical compressive stress in the ice at depth h is $\varrho_i g h$, where ϱ_i is the density of ice. The horizontal stress component thus exceeds the vertical component by an amount $\Delta p = (\varrho_\omega - \varrho_i) g h$. This is equivalent to a shear stress $\frac{1}{2} \Delta p$ on planes at 45° to the horizontal. At depths greater than 200 m, this shear stress will exceed 1 bar and so will cause appreciable ice flow. The hole will enlarge. (This argument is analogous to the simple explanation, given in Chapter 6, of why crevasse depths seldom exceed 25 m. The crevasse was assumed to be free of water.) Passages, not necessarily vertical, will open up in this way, provided the hydrostatic pressure of the water is sufficiently great.

Glen also suggested that deep ice-dammed lakes may drain through a channel formed by the same mechanism at the base of the glacier. (If the water temperature is above 0°C, melting will help to enlarge the channel.) An alternative explanation is that drainage starts when the water becomes deep enough (9/10 of the height of the ice dam) to float the glacier. Observations show that, at least in some cases, the discharge of water builds up gradually to a maximum and continues at maximum rate until the lake is completely empty. Such behaviour favours Glen's explanation.

These considerations suggest the following picture of the water system in a temperate glacier. During the melt season, the glacier contains a considerable amount of free water. The glacier acts rather like a reservoir which is drained continuously by the streams emerging at its terminus and is refilled daily by meltwater. The water is contained in crevasses, moulins, and cavities within the ice and at the bed. Some of these are probably isolated, at least temporarily, while others are connected by a system of channels within the glacier. As long as the cavities and channels contain enough water, the ice cannot flow in and close them. They will close during the winter and be gradually reopened by meltwater at the beginning of the following summer. The system will develop during the summer as increasing amounts of meltwater enlarge old channels and open up new ones. Floods probably result from the draining of a series of previously isolated cavities, for example, when the barriers between a series of waterfilled crevasses are breached successively.

This picture is largely speculative. The way in which water flows through a glacier, the time it takes, and how the water affects the ice temperature are matters that deserve further study.

Note Added in Proof

Since this chapter was written, Lliboutry has further developed the theory of glcier aliding in two important papers: *Journal of Glaciology*, vol. 7, pp. 21–58, 1968 and International Association of Scientific Hydrology, publication no. 79, pp. 33–48, 1968.

FIG. 8.1. Variegated Glacier, Alaska, before surge (29 August 1964). Photo by Austin Post, U.S. Geological Survey.

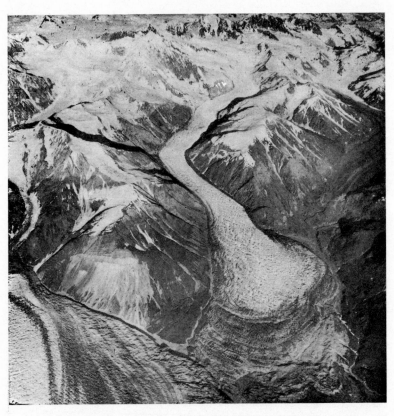

Fig. 8.2. Variegated Glacier, Alaska, during surge (22 August 1965).
Photo by Austin Post, U.S. Geological Survey.

CHAPTER 8

GLACIER SURGES

"Out of whose womb came the ice?"

Book of Job.

Introduction

Isolated examples of glaciers making sudden rapid advances have been known since at least the beginning of this century. A glacier, after showing little sign of activity for many years, starts to move rapidly and its surface becomes transformed to a chaotic mass of crevasses and ice pinnacles. Typically, the ice in the lower reaches of the glacier moves several kilometres in a few months or, at most, two or three years. The rapid movement then suddenly stops. This is quite different from a normal advance in which the terminus may move forward a few metres per year. Figures 8.1 and 8.2 show the same glacier in its stagnant and active conditions.

Such behaviour is often called a "catastrophic advance", while "galloping glacier" is popular with journalists. The term "surge" is preferable. Before a surge, the glacier, for several kilometres above its terminus, often consists of stagnant ice, covered with a thick layer of rubble. This ice becomes reactivated and thickens greatly during the surge, and the boundary between active and stagnant ice advances as the surge proceeds. But this active terminus may never move beyond the limits of the previously stagnant ice. To speak of an advance is not correct in this case.

Observations in the last few years have shown that surges occur more often than previously believed. Nevertheless, they are still rare events. The majority of surges are completed in one or two years and surging glaciers are usually in remote areas.

Moreover, the glacier surface is inaccessible during a surge. For these reasons, detailed data are lacking and no one yet understands the mechanism of a surge. A few theories have been put forward, but none is really adequate.

Description

Surges have been reported from many parts of the world. One of the earliest descriptions is that of Tarr and Martin (1914, pp. 168–97). They observed surges in nine glaciers in southern Alaska between 1900 and 1910. Lliboutry (1958b) has reported that five glaciers in the central Andes in Chile made surges at various times between 1927 and 1957. In the Karakorams, Desio (1954) has described Kutiah Glacier which advanced about 12 km in 3 months in 1953. In the Pamirs, the surge of Medvezhii Glacier in 1963 has been well documented by Dolgushin and others (1963). These authors also state that a glacier in the Tien Shan surged in the 1950's. Several glaciers and small ice caps in Spitsbergen have surged, including one which advanced 21 km, the greatest movement so far recorded in a surge, between 1935 and 1938 (Glen, 1941). In the Canadian Arctic, Hattersley–Smith (1964) has described the surge of Otto Fiord Glacier in northwest Ellesmere Island.

Since 1960 Post (1965), during annual aerial reconnaissance flights, has observed surges in at least twenty glaciers in Alaska and Canada. In addition he has identified some hundred glaciers which probably surge, although they have not been observed to do so. This is of course only an extremely small percentage of all the glaciers in the area. Almost all the surging glaciers are in the Alaska Range or the St. Elias Mountains: none has been found in the Rocky Mountains or the Coast Mountains. While the apparent lack of surging glaciers in some areas may reflect a lack of observations there, the distribution of surging glaciers is certainly not random. Glaciers in the same area do not necessarily surge at the same time. Susitna and Black Rapids Glaciers in Alaska originate in the same icefield. One surged in 1936–7, the other in 1953 (Post, 1960). Most surging glaciers are relatively large (several tens of kilometres long).

Medial moraines on surging glaciers have a distinctive pattern. Instead of smooth lines, more or less parallel to the valley walls, the moraines are deformed into large bulb-like loops, as seen in Fig. 8.1. A loop is probably formed by flow of ice from a tributary glacier while the main glacier is quiescent. The surge of the main glacier carries the loop several kilometres down the main valley. The tributary forms a new loop after the surge. In addition, some loops may be formed by surges of tributary glaciers. In many cases, nearly identical loops are seen at intervals along the glacier. This suggests that surging is a periodic phenomenon, although very few glaciers have actually been observed to surge more than once. (Tyeen Glacier in southeast Alaska is one: it surged in 1948 and 1966.) These distinctive moraine patterns, combined with a long stretch of stagnant dirt-covered ice and high trim-lines at the terminus, are indications of a glacier that surges.

The most detailed information so far published is probably Post's description of the surge of Muldrow Glacier in Alaska during the winter of 1956-7 (Post, 1960). Muldrow Glacier is some 63 km long and spans an elevation range of over 5000 m. The upper part of the glacier lies on steep mountain slopes; but for the last 40 km of its course the glacier flows in a deep valley where its average surface slope is only about 2°. Post compared air photos taken before and immediately after the surge: Figs. 8.3 and 8.4 show his results. As far as could be determined, the part of the glacier above the break in slope at the head of the valley was unaffected by the surge. On Muldrow Glacier, the affected area is roughly the same as the ablation area. However, observations on other glaciers suggest that it is the break in slope rather than the equilibrium line which determines the limits of the surge.

Points on the moraine patterns were used to obtain the surface movement vectors in Fig. 8.3. The ice in the region of profile *AB* moved the furthest. Flow was mainly compressing below this profile: flow above was extending (see Chapter 6). However, the total movement did not vary a great deal throughout the affected part of the main glacier. This is confirmed by the fact that the

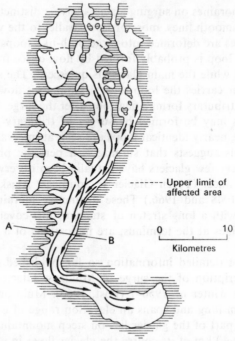

------- Upper limit of
affected area

A

B

0   10

Kilometres

FIG. 8.3. Muldrow Glacier, Alaska: displacement vectors during surge. From Post (1960).

chief features of the surface moraine patterns were preserved. Total movement of ice was about 6·5 km in not more than 9 months. This is an average of about 20 m day^{-1}; velocities were probably several times this value during part of the surge. Such values are about 100 times the velocity of a normal glacier. Other than in surges, comparable velocities have been measured only on the floating tongues of one or two large glaciers in West Greenland.

Figure 8.4 shows the longitudinal profile of the affected area before and immediately after the surge. In the upper part, the surface was lowered by 50 or 60 m. Fringes of ice were left hanging on the valley walls. Tributary glaciers formed vertical ice cliffs at their junction with the main glacier, their ends having

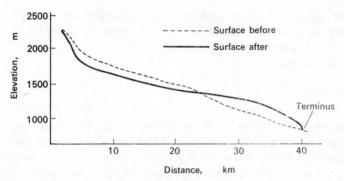

FIG. 8.4. Muldrow Glacier, Alaska: change of surface elevation during surge. From Post (1960).

been sheared off. This was only a temporary condition. The tributaries then started to move rapidly, and their surface levels dropped. In its lower reaches, the surface of the main glacier was raised by as much as 50 or 60 m. The line AB in Fig. 8.3 marks the place where the surface elevation was unchanged. As far as could be determined, the gain of ice below AB was equal to the loss of ice above it. These changes of surface level are consistent with the pattern of extending and compressing flow shown by the surface movement vectors.

Dolgushin and others (1963) observed some other interesting features during the surge of Medvezhii Glacier. The boundary between the affected and unaffected parts of the glacier, which coincided with an icefall, was marked by a large transverse fracture. The ice on the downstream side was displaced about 80 m vertically downwards, relative to the upstream ice. In addition a continuous fracture, 8 km long, 10 m wide, and possibly reaching the glacier bed, extended along the glacier near each side. As on Muldrow Glacier, the ice thickness decreased in the upper part of the affected area and increased in the lower part. During the surge, Dolgushin also observed four shallow "waves", about 2 km in length and 50 to 70 m high, on the glacier surface. It was inferred that these waves travelled the whole length of the glacier tongue, that is, about four times the distance the ice moved. Medvezhii Glacier apparently made a minor surge in 1951, in addition to the surge observed in 1963.

The features observed on these two glaciers appear to be typical of many surges.

Theories

No adequate explanation of surges has yet been put forward. Dynamic conditions in these particular glaciers appear to be somehow unstable. Conditions at the bed of the glacier change in some way and allow much greater sliding velocities than normal. It is not known whether a surge is triggered by some external factor, or whether conditions build up over a period of years until some critical threshold is reached.

Tarr and Martin explained the surges they observed in Alaska as a delayed response to the avalanching on to the glaciers of large quantities of snow and ice, during a major earthquake in 1899. There was no evidence that large avalanches had in fact occurred. Moreover, two of the glaciers originate in wide basins; it is unlikely that avalanches could add significant amounts of material to them. Again, there seems to be little correlation in time or space between surges and other earthquakes in the area (Post, 1965). For these reasons the "earthquake-advance theory" is now rather out of favour. Some connection between certain surges and tectonic activity should not be completely discounted however. Post (1960) has pointed out that nearly all the surging glaciers in the Alaska Range lie along one fault system.

Robin (1955) has suggested that a temperature change at the glacier bed might start a surge. If, in a glacier frozen to its bed, the temperature of the basal ice were raised, the velocity would increase because the flow law depends sensitively on temperature. The increased flow would increase the amount of heat produced by strain-work. The temperature would continue to rise and the melting point might finally be reached. The glacier would then start to slip on its bed. As possible causes of the initial temperature increase, Robin suggested an increase in velocity resulting from an increase in the glacier's net mass balance, or else an increase in the amount of heat conducted to the glacier bed from the valley walls, after a series of warm summers. Others have suggested an increase in the amount of geothermal heat. However, this quantity does not normally vary over short periods, except in volcanic areas. Lliboutry (1965, p. 661) thinks that the temperature at the bed might increase if part of the glacier were transformed from an accumulation to an ablation area. He has suggested that this might start a surge.

There is more than one objection to explanations of this type. Although no measurements have been made, it is likely that the surging glaciers in many areas are at the melting temperature, at least at their beds, whether a surge is in progress or not. Again, on this theory, surging glaciers might be expected to move at speeds comparable with sliding velocities in other glaciers, rather than a hundred times as fast.

Weertman (1962a) has suggested that an increase in the amount of water at the glacier bed could cause a surge. This is based on his theory of glacier sliding, given in Chapter 7. On this theory, the sliding velocity is largely controlled by irregularities of a certain size on the glacier bed. Any water layer is normally thinner than the controlling obstacle size and so doesn't affect the sliding velocity very much. Suppose, however, that the thickness of the water layer were to increase until it exceeded the controlling obstacle size. The sliding velocity would then be controlled by obstacles larger than critical size; much higher velocities would then be possible. This theory, unlike Robin's, would explain surges in temperate glaciers.

Weertman made a mathematical analysis of the problem and concluded that this mechanism could account for a surge only under a rather special set of conditions. These are:

1. The glacier should be long (10 to 30 km).
2. The base should be at the pressure melting point.
3. The water at the bed should flow as a sheet, not in channels.
4. The basal shear stress should be about twice the normal value.
5. The glacier bed should be smoother with respect to large bumps than with respect to small ones. (This means that large bumps should be few and far between.)

A surge must only be possible under certain restricted conditions; otherwise more glaciers would make surges. However, the above set of conditions is perhaps too restrictive. While many surging glaciers are between 10 and 30 km long, surges have occurred in smaller and also in much larger glaciers than this. Again, Weertman's mathematical analysis rests on the assumption that all the water at the bed originates from melting of ice there. Any water penetrating from the surface is ignored. This is hardly realistic. The question of the controlling obstacle size is also in dispute (see Chapter 7). Weertman thinks it is of the order of 1 cm; Kamb and LaChapelle, about 50 cm. The idea of 1 cm of water at the glacier bed is acceptable, but a layer about 50 cm thick seems impossible. Thus if Kamb and LaChapelle are correct, Weertman's explanation can hardly apply. In short, although Weertman's theory of glacier sliding is widely accepted, at least qualitatively, his explanation of surges is not.

One might ask, particularly in view of Dolgushin's observations, whether a surge is not merely a case of exceptionally large kinematic waves (bulges of increased thickness) passing down the glacier. The kinematic wave theory, given in Chapter 11, describes how a glacier reacts to a mass balance change which is assumed for simplicity to be the same at all points on the glacier. According to the theory, an increase in mass balance causes the glacier to thicken everywhere. The amount of thickening varies in time and at different points along the glacier, but the effect is always greatest at the terminus. Similarly a decrease in mass balance results in thinning everywhere. Surges, on the other hand, appear to be confined to part of the glacier and merely result in a redistribution of ice.

Again, to compare the condition of the glacier during a surge with its condition beforehand: a decrease in surface slope and, in places, in ice thickness have been accompanied by a hundredfold increase in velocity. The normal theories of glacier flow and sliding, and the kinematic wave theory, do not apply in this case.

Kinematic waves resulting from an increase in mass balance thus seem to be excluded as the cause of a surge. There must be other reasons why the surge starts and why the velocity is abnormally high. However, it is quite possible that, during the surge, kinematic waves may be propagated down the glacier.

Whether surges are preceded by an increase in mass balance is not known. Mass balance measurements have not been made on any surging glacier, so one has to fall back on records from distant weather stations. These may bear little relation to the climate on the glacier. Miller (1958) showed that precipitation in south-east Alaska was above average between 1881 and 1886. He suggested that the surges observed by Tarr and Martin in the early 1900's might be related to this. However, Post (1960) could find no sign of any climatic change favourable to glacier growth in the years before the Muldrow Glacier surge. Dolgushin states that the surge of Medvezhii Glacier was not preceded by an increase in precipitation.

Unknowns

Before we can understand surges, more field data are needed. The best approach appears to be to select a glacier which is likely to surge, so that measurements can be made before, during, and after the surge. To start making observations after the surge is in progress is too late, and measurement of such quantities as ice thickness and temperature then becomes very difficult. The risk that the glacier may not surge, and thus render the initial measurements valueless, will have to be accepted.

Questions requiring answers are whether the mass balance increases for several years before a surge, whether the ice temperature is changing, whether the glacier is sliding on its bed before the surge, and whether the topography of the bed is in any way peculiar. Any possible connection between surges and earthquakes or abnormal avalanching is also worth further investigation. We don't know where a surge begins. Effects might be propagated back up the glacier for some distance, as happens on the tributaries, so it is not certain that the surge starts at the upper limit of the affected area.

There is virtually no information on how surface elevation and slope, and ice velocity, vary at different parts of the glacier during a surge. Comparative measurements before and afterwards are also needed. In view of Weertman's theory one would like to know the thickness of any water layer at the glacier bed. It is hard to see how this could be determined; but at least the amount of water discharged from beneath the glacier before, during, and after a surge might be measured. The high velocities are unexplained. Nor do we know why surging glaciers are found only in certain areas, whether surges in one glacier occur at regular or irregular intervals, or whether a glacier which surges can also make a normal slow advance.

It is uncertain whether a surge is a completely different phenomenon from a normal slow advance, or whether there are intermediate types of behaviour. Most surges, including the ones we have described, seem to be quite different from normal advances. But in some other cases the distinction is less clear. Moltke Glacier in northwest Greenland would not normally be regarded as a surging glacier: but Mock (1966) has shown that, during the past 40 years, the velocity near its terminus has ranged from 30 m y^{-1} to 1 km y^{-1}. The fact that this glacier ends in the sea may introduce complications however. It has recently been reported from New Zealand that Franz Josef Glacier is advancing about 2 m day^{-1}. This seems slow for a surge, but fast for a normal advance. The surge of Walsh Glacier, near the Alaska-Yukon boundary, has continued for 4 years, a long period compared with most surges (Post, 1966, 1967). Again, Meier and others (1966) have recently reported "repeated pulses of activity which may be related to surges" in Bering Glacier in Alaska. However, the terminus is only advancing about 100 m y^{-1}. Somewhat similar pulses may travel down Malaspina Glacier, Alaska, although they appear to have little effect at the terminus. Thus some glaciers seem to behave in ways which cannot be classified either as a normal advance or as a surge.

CHAPTER 9

THE FLOW OF ICE SHEETS

"The frightful ice that covers the whole face of the land."
HANS EGEDE, *A Description of Greenland* (1745).

Introduction

The theory of glacier flow has been discussed in previous chapters. We now turn to the subject of the flow of an ice sheet. There is no fundamental difference between a glacier and an ice sheet, and the distinction may be hard to make in some cases. The previous theory still applies, except in obvious cases such as the discussion of how the valley walls modify the flow, and we shall use results derived earlier. The present chapter involves a shift of emphasis, however: different questions are now important. Previously we were concerned mainly with the situation at one point. Now we consider the shape of the ice sheet as a whole, how it is influenced by accumulation and ablation, and by the underlying topography. We shall also discuss the flow of a floating ice shelf.

As before, the theoretical approach provides valuable insights into the behaviour of ice sheets. The differences between the simplified models and a real ice sheet must be kept in mind, however.

Theoretical Profiles of Ice Sheets

In this section we consider an ice sheet in a steady state (that is, the thickness at each point does not change with time) resting on a horizontal bed. Figure 9.1 represents a cross-section of the ice sheet. To restrict the treatment to two dimensions, the ice sheet is assumed to be a long ridge perpendicular to the plane of the paper.

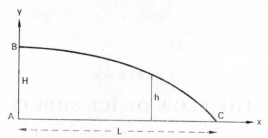

FIG. 9.1. Coordinate system: ideal ice sheet.

The x-axis is horizontal, the y-axis vertical, and the origin is on the base at the centre of the ice sheet. The total width is $2L$, the ice thickness is h in general and H at the centre. Stresses and velocities are assumed to vary only slowly with x. Since the shear stress at the bed is proportional to h and $\mathrm{d}h/\mathrm{d}x$, this assumption implies that $|\,\mathrm{d}h/\mathrm{d}x\,| \ll 1$ and $|\,h\,\mathrm{d}^2h/\mathrm{d}x^2\,| \ll |\,\mathrm{d}h/\mathrm{d}x\,|$. These restrictions are not met near the centre and edge of the ice sheet. Thus discrepancies between theoretical and observed profiles may be expected in these regions.

Orowan (1949) considered the case of a perfectly plastic ice sheet. In Fig. 9.1 the total horizontal force on the central plane AB, per unit length perpendicular to the plane of the paper, is

$$\int_0^H \varrho g(H-y)\,\mathrm{d}y = \tfrac{1}{2}\,\varrho g H^2$$

Here ϱ is density (assumed constant) and g is acceleration due to gravity. The only other horizontal force on AB is the force due to the shear stress on the base AC. This stress is τ_0, the yield stress. Thus, for equilibrium,

$$\tfrac{1}{2}\,\varrho g H^2 = \tau_0 L$$
$$H = (2\tau_0 L/\varrho g)^{1/2}$$

If $\tau_0 = 1$ bar, $2\tau_0/\varrho g = 10$ m and the equation becomes

$$H = 5L^{1/2} \tag{1}$$

where H and L are in metres.

As a first check, this formula was applied to central Greenland (latitude 72°N). Here L is 450 km and the formula gives about 3000 m for H. The true value is slightly over 3200 m. The agreement is satisfying, but somewhat fortuitous in view of the drastic simplifications made in the calculation.

By a similar argument, the profile of a perfectly plastic ice sheet of width $2L$ can be shown to be the parabola

$$(h/H)^2 = 1 - x/L \tag{2}$$

where H is given by (1).

The next step is to replace the approximation of perfect plasticity by the actual flow law of ice. However, the temperature distribution in an ice sheet creates a problem, as the flow law depends on temperature. In the study of flow in a glacier this difficulty is avoided by assuming that the glacier is isothermal. As many glaciers in temperate regions are at or near the pressure melting point throughout, this is a valid simplification. But ice sheets are confined to polar regions. Near the surface of a large ice sheet, the temperature may be 30 deg lower than it is at the base. The assumption that an ice sheet is isothermal is not realistic.

The temperature distribution in an ice sheet is discussed in Chapter 10. The main feature is that the highest temperature occurs at the base. In addition, the shear stress is greatest at the base. As strain rate depends strongly on temperature and on shear stress, the rate of change of horizontal velocity with depth, $\partial u/\partial y$, should be large near the bottom of the ice sheet but small elsewhere. For this reason, Nye (1959b) proposed the simplifying assumption that all the shear takes place at the base. In other words, u is the same at all depths. Nye further suggested that, in this case, Weertman's equation for the slip of a glacier over its bed (equation (5″) of Chapter 7) could be used to give the velocity of the ice sheet, whether the motion consists of slip on the bed or of rapid shear in the lowest layers of ice. This equation is

$$u = A'\tau_b^m \tag{3}$$

where A' and m are constants and τ_b is the basal shear stress. As the base is horizontal, the surface slope is dh/dx and so

$$\tau_b = -\varrho gh(dh/dx) \tag{4}$$

The ice sheet is assumed to be in a steady state. Thus the amount of ice which accumulates on the surface between the crest and any point P must be equal to the amount of ice flowing through a vertical section at P. For simplicity, assume that a uniform thickness of ice, b, is added to the surface in one year. Then, since u is assumed constant with depth,

$$bx = hu = A'h[-\varrho gh(dh/dx)]^m$$

This differential equation gives the steady state profile. Thus

$$h^{2+1/m} = (2m+1)(m+1)^{-1}(\varrho g)^{-1}(b/A')^{1/m}(L^{1+1/m}-x^{1+1/m}) \tag{5}$$

But $h = H$ when $x = 0$, so we can write the equation as

$$(h/H)^{2+1/m}+(x/L)^{1+1/m} = 1 \tag{6}$$

Weertman's results suggest that m is about 2. The equation becomes

$$(h/H)^{2.5}+(x/L)^{1.5} = 1 \tag{7}$$

For the case of perfect plasticity, $m \to \infty$ and the profile reduces to the parabola obtained previously.

Before we consider the implications of these results, we shall mention a few other possible profiles.

The effects of any longitudinal stress σ_x are neglected in the above treatment. Weertman (1961a) attempted to allow for such a stress by replacing (3) by a more general, but empirical, relation. He found no significant difference for a large ice sheet. If the ice sheet is small ($L \approx 15$ km), the profile obtained by Weertman has a smaller curvature than that given by (6).

Instead of using the equation for basal slip (3), Vialov (1958) started with the flow law

$$\partial u/\partial y = A[-\varrho gy(dh/dx)]^n$$

The shear stress is assumed to be much larger than the other stress deviators. It is also assumed that the ice cap does not slide on its base. As A depends on temperature, a mean value has to be used. The mean is weighted in favour of its value in the lowest layers of ice because differential movement is largely confined to these layers. By an argument similar to that used to derive (5) and (6), Vialov obtained the equation

$$(h/H)^{2(1+1/n)} + (x/L)^{1+1/n} = 1 \tag{8}$$

with $n = 3$, this becomes

$$(h/H)^{2 \cdot 6} + (x/L)^{1 \cdot 3} = 1 \tag{9}$$

which differs only slightly from (7).

The ellipse

$$(h/H)^2 + (x/L)^2 = 1 \tag{10}$$

has been shown to fit portions of the Antarctic ice sheet. This equation can be derived by starting with the relation

$$u = A''(dh/dx)$$

The interpretation is that u, the sliding velocity, is assumed to vary directly as basal shear stress and inversely as hydrostatic pressure. As a result, u depends on surface slope only, not on ice thickness. This relation was proposed by Bodvarsson (1955).

Figure 9.2 shows the various profiles. As the difference between (7) and (9) is hardly perceptible at this scale, only one of them is drawn.

Some important conclusions can be drawn from (5). This equation shows that h is proportional to $b^{1/(2m+1)}$. If $m = 2$, thickness is proportional to the fifth root of the net mass balance. Vialov's analysis gives a comparable result (the eighth root). (The approximation of perfect plasticity provides the extreme case in which the profile is independent of mass balance.) Thus the steady state thickness of an ice sheet is very insensitive to its mass balance.

Equation (5) also shows that h varies inversely as the fifth root of A'. The value of A' is determined by the roughness of the bed of

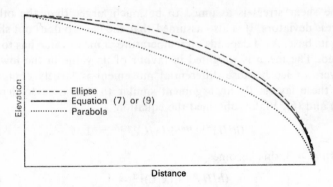

FIG. 9.2. Theoretical profiles of ice sheets.

the ice sheet and other factors. The value of A, the comparable constant in the flow law as used in Vialov's analysis, decreases with decrease in temperature. The analysis shows that, other things being equal, the colder the ice sheet the thicker it should be. But the dependence is not very sensitive: a decrease in temperature of about 20 deg will increase h by about 35 per cent.

The condition for a steady state namely,

$$u = bx/h$$

shows that u increases steadily from the centre of the ice sheet to its equilibrium line. (Below the equilibrium line, b is negative.) Equation (3) shows that the basal shear stress must behave similarly, provided that A' is constant.

Table 9.1 shows calculated steady state velocities in an ice sheet of total width 2000 km for a net mass balance of 15 cm of ice. For simplicity, a parabolic profile was taken. Such an ice sheet would be 4700 m thick at its centre. (The greatest thickness so far measured in Antarctica is 4300 m.) Table 9.1 shows that, because of the low accumulation rate and great ice thickness, only low velocities are needed over much of the ice sheet to maintain a steady state. A particle of ice would take about 75,000 years to travel from $x = 50$ km to the edge of this ice sheet. About 60 per cent of this time would be spent in reaching $x = 300$ km.

On this model, multiplying the accumulation by any factor will multiply the velocities by the same factor.

TABLE 9.1. STEADY STATE
VELOCITIES IN ICE CAP OF
PARABOLIC PROFILE
(Total width = 2000 km; Net
mass balance = 15 cm ice)

Distance from centre km	Velocity $m\,y^{-1}$
0	0
100	3
200	7
400	16
600	30
800	57
900	90
950	135

Discussion of Assumptions

Before we compare some measured ice sheet profiles with the theoretical ones we shall summarize the assumptions underlying the derivation of the preceding equations.

1. The profile follows a flow line.
2. The base of the ice sheet is horizontal.
3. The ice sheet is in a steady state.
4. Mass balance is constant over the ice sheet.
5. Temperature, roughness of the bed and other factors which might influence the velocity (i.e. which might change the value of A and A') are constant over the ice sheet.
6. Stresses and velocities vary only slowly with horizontal distance.

To what extent will these conditions hold in a real ice sheet?
A considerable number of traverses have been made across ice sheets; comparatively few have followed flow lines. If a reliable

map of the ice sheet is available, the best method may be to draw profiles from it.

Some small ice caps rest on beds which are roughly horizontal, and bedrock in the central part of Greenland appears to be relatively smooth, if not strictly horizontal. The bedrock topography under much of Antarctica, on the other hand, seems to be extremely rough. The Greenland ice sheet is largely fringed by mountains. Most of the ice flow is channelled into some twenty very large outlet glaciers. Thus it is not correct to picture Greenland as a large regularly-shaped ice sheet extending to sea level.

No ice sheet is ever in a steady state. The important factor is the relative magnitude of the terms in the continuity equation. This equation, which expresses the fact that there is no change in mass of an element of ice, is

$$\partial q/\partial x + \partial h/\partial t = b$$

Here, the flow q is $\int\limits_0^h u \, dy$, and b is net mass balance. If the flow term $\partial q/\partial x$ is comparable with b, the rate of change of thickness $\partial h/\partial t$ will be small. The ice sheet should be near enough a steady state for the theory to apply. If however $\partial q/\partial x$ is small, the surface elevation at each point will vary in response to the accumulation and ablation there, and local variations in these factors will determine the profile. In this case the profile will not conform to that deduced from flow theory. Lliboutry (1965, pp. 458–60) has drawn a similar distinction between *glaciers évacuateurs*, in which flow is important, and *glaciers réservoirs* in which it is insignificant. In time, of course, a stagnant ice sheet may build up to such a thickness that flow becomes important.

The mass balance is never constant over an ice sheet. In Antarctica, for example, the accumulation rate near the coast is roughly ten times that in the interior. And there is net ablation in parts of other ice sheets. Similarly, such factors as temperature and roughness of the bed will vary from place to place in a real ice sheet.

The final assumption, that stresses and velocities vary only slowly with distance, is probably valid at many places in a polar ice sheet. On the other hand, we shall see later that there appear to be places where the rate of change of longitudinal stress with distance is great enough to affect the surface topography appreciably.

Measured Profiles of Ice Sheets

Figure 9.3 shows the profile, roughly following a flow line, of the Antarctic ice sheet for about 850 km inland from Mirny (latitude 66·5°S, longitude 93°E), as measured by one of the

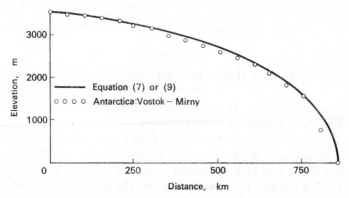

FIG. 9.3. Profile of Antarctic ice sheet between Vostok and Mirny, compared with theoretical profile. Data from Vialov (1958).

Soviet Antarctic Expeditions. Equation (7) fits the data well. Vialov (1958) has shown that an ellipse is also a satisfactory fit. This is one profile from many available. Most have approximately the same shape, and theoretical curves have been fitted to some. Imbert (1959) found that an ellipse fitted a 500 km profile of the Antarctic ice sheet in Terre Adelie. Kapitsa (1964) showed that the profiles of Drygalski and Bowman Islands in the Antarctic were ellipses. Haefeli (1961) used a somewhat complicated function to represent the profile of the ice sheet in central Greenland.

In view of the approximations made, the theoretical profiles agree surprisingly well with the observed ones. Such agreement supports the basic idea that the shape of an ice sheet is largely determined by the plastic properties of ice. Variations in accumu-

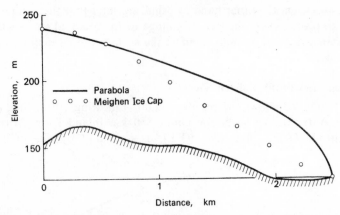

FIG. 9.4. Profile of Meighen Ice Cap, Canada, compared with theoretical profile.

lation, temperature, the nature of the bed, and other factors are relatively unimportant in many cases.

Figures 9.4 and 9.5 show two ice caps which do not conform to the theoretical profile. Figure 9.4 represents the small ice cap (area 75 km^2) on Meighen Island in Arctic Canada. The bed of the ice cap is not very far from horizontal. The profile does not fit the theoretical pattern, because the ice cap is not in a steady state. The flow is less than 30 cm y^{-1}. As a result, the level of the ice cap at each point is determined by the mass balance at that point.

The profile in Fig. 9.5 differs from the theoretical one for another reason. This figure shows the outline of the surface and base of

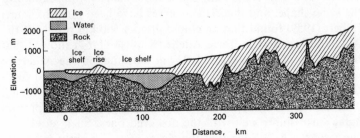

FIG. 9.5. Profile of Antarctic ice sheet in Queen Maud Land. From Robin (1958).

the ice sheet in Queen Maud Land, Antarctica, as measured by Robin (1958). The bedrock topography is extremely rough and has a considerable effect on the surface profile. This relationship is discussed in detail in the next section. Figure 9.5 also shows a floating ice shelf and an ice rise, features which will be described later.

Relation between Surface and Bed Topography

If ice is assumed to be a perfectly plastic material, the relation between surface and bed topography becomes very simple. At every point, the basal shear stress is equal to the yield stress, which is constant. Thus the product of ice thickness and surface slope is constant. Where the ice is thick the surface slope is small: where the ice is thin the surface is relatively steep. It follows that points of inflexion of the surface should correspond approximately to high or low points of the bed. Robin (1958) verified that this was the case on the ice sheet in Queen Maud Land. (The scale of Fig. 9.5 is too small to show this.) Bourgoin (1956) came to the same conclusion from measurements on the Greenland ice sheet.

Nye (1959b) has made an analysis of this problem. He used, not the approximation of perfect plasticity, but the relation between velocity and basal shear stress which he used to derive the surface profile for a horizontal bed, namely

$$u = A' \tau_b^m \qquad (3)$$

Figure 9.6 represents a bedrock ridge, of limited width and of height $p(x)$, perpendicular to the direction of ice flow. For comparison, we also consider a "reference ice sheet" in which the ridge is replaced by a horizontal plane. Let h, α denote ice thickness and surface slope. When quantities refer to the reference ice sheet the suffix o is used. The height of the ridge p is assumed to be small compared with h_0. The values of h and α at any point over the ridge can be expressed as deviations from h_0 and α_0, by writing

$$h = h_0 + h_1 \qquad \alpha = \alpha_0 + \alpha_1$$

where h_1, α_1 are small compared with h_0 and α_0. If ε is the change

11*

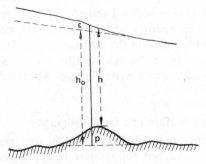

FIG. 9.6. Change $\varepsilon(x)$ in surface elevation of an ice sheet produced by a small ridge $p(x)$ on the bed. The ice thickness is h. The thickness of the "reference ice sheet" is h_0.

in elevation of the upper surface due to the ridge, Figure 9.6 shows that

$$h_0 + \varepsilon = h + p = h_0 + h_1 + p$$

$$\varepsilon = h_1 + p$$

The flow of ice q through any cross-section depends on the mass balance, and also on any change of surface level with time, over that part of the ice sheet which lies between the highest point and the cross-section. Neither mass balance nor changes of surface level in time over this area should be modified by a bedrock ridge at one point. Thus the ridge should not change the flow and so $q = q_0$. But

$$q = uh = A'h\tau_b^m = A'h(-\varrho g h\alpha)^m$$

Thus

$$h^{m+1}\alpha^m = h_0^{m+1}\alpha_0^m \tag{11}$$

and, since h_1/h_0 and α_1/α_0 are small,

$$(m+1)h_1/h_0 + m\alpha_1/\alpha_0 = 0 \tag{12}$$

But $\alpha_0 = -\mathrm{d}h_0/\mathrm{d}x$ and $\alpha_1 = -\mathrm{d}\varepsilon/\mathrm{d}x = -\dfrac{\mathrm{d}}{\mathrm{d}x}(h_1 + p)$

Thus $[(m+1)\, h_1/mh_0]\,(\mathrm{d}h_0/\mathrm{d}x) + \mathrm{d}h_1/\mathrm{d}x + \mathrm{d}p/\mathrm{d}x = 0$

This integrates to

$$h_0^{1+1/m}h_1 = -\int_0^p h_0^{1+1/m}\,\mathrm{d}p$$

because $h_1 = 0$ sufficiently far downstream from the ridge. Now h_0 changes only slowly over the ridge, so it can be taken outside the integration. It follows that h_1 is approximately equal to $-p$, and so $\varepsilon(= h_1+p)$ is approximately zero. This means that the change in surface elevation is much smaller than the height of the bedrock ridge which produces it.

It follows from (12), with $m = 2$, that

$$\alpha_1/\alpha_0 \approx 1{\cdot}5p/h_0 \tag{13}$$

Also, the condition that flow is constant can be written as

$$h\tau^m = h_0\tau_0^m$$

where τ denotes basal shear stress. Thus, if τ_1 is the change in shear stress produced by the ridge,

$$\tau_1/\tau_0 = -h_1/mh_0 \approx 0{\cdot}5p/h_0 \tag{14}$$

Thus, for example, a ridge 300 m high covered by 3000 m of ice should change the surface elevation by an amount small compared with 300 m, the surface slope by about 15 per cent and the basal shear stress by about 5 per cent. If we write (13) in the form

$$p \approx 0{\cdot}7h_0\alpha_1/\alpha_0$$

the height of a buried ridge can be calculated from the change of surface slope which it produces. Note that the bedrock ridge is assumed to be small compared with the ice thickness. There are many places in real ice sheets where this will not be true. Figure 9.5 is an example. This theory is not expected to apply in such places.

These predictions have not yet been confirmed in detail. In fact, some recent observations in Antarctica appear to conflict with them. Lister (1959) observed large undulations on the surface of the South Polar Plateau. These have a mean amplitude of 20 or

25 m and mean wavelength of about 12 km. They therefore represent changes of slope comparable with the surface slope, over distances of the order of the ice thickness. Any undulations of this size which do not result from bedrock irregularities should be eliminated by flow. This is because the surface slope on the upstream side of a crest will be less than average, and greater than average on the downstream side. Thus the basal shear stress, and therefore the velocity, will be greater on the downstream side. Thus the crest will be stretched and flattened. (Small undulations such as sastrugi are not eliminated in this way because they don't change the shear stress appreciably.) As the undulations persist, they were thought to indicate buried mountains. Seismic soundings by Robinson (1966), however, showed no such mountains.

One suggested explanation is that ice flow in this area may be extremely small. Thus the undulations, which may merely result from local variations in accumulation, are not eliminated. This would imply that this part of the ice sheet is not in a steady state, and so its thickness must be slowly increasing. The fact that calculated shear stresses are low (a mean of 0·8 bar) lends some support to the suggestion that flow may be very small. The temperature of the ice near the surface is $-51°C$, the ice thickness is roughly 2500 m, and the annual accumulation is about 15 cm. If the only source of heat at the base of the ice sheet is the geothermal flux, Figure 10.2 (page 182) leads one to expect a temperature of about $-25°C$ there. (This is only a rough calculation because Fig. 10.2 refers to a steady state.) The low temperature and low shear stress combine to make the velocity very small. The question will only be settled when velocities in the area have been measured accurately. This is extremely difficult because of the great distance from any ice-free land.

Although the calculated basal shear stress is about 1 bar in many parts of polar ice sheets, values significantly lower than this are not uncommon. From measurements of ice thickness and surface slope in the central part of North Greenland, Bull (1957) calculated shear stresses of 0·2 to 0·8 bar. This meant that earlier predictions of ice thickness in this area, based on an assumed shear stress of 1 bar, were much too great. Basal shear stresses over much of the Barnes Ice Cap in Baffin Island appear to be about 0·7 bar.

To date, study of the relation between the surface form of an ice sheet and its bed has been hampered by insufficient detail of the shape of the bed. Recently developed radar methods of ice sounding enable a continuous profile of both surface and bed to be drawn. The combination of such data with measurements of velocity and strain rate should permit a better understanding of this matter. Robin (1967) has recently analysed some data of this kind.

The analysis is based on equation (35) of Chapter 6 which can be written, approximately, as

$$\alpha_s = \tau_b/\varrho g h - (\varrho g)^{-1} \frac{d}{dx} (\bar{\sigma}_x - \bar{\sigma}_y) \tag{15}$$

If the second term on the right-hand side is zero and if $\tau_b = 1$ bar, we obtain the usual formula relating surface slope and ice thickness. Normally the formula is used to estimate ice thickness from surface slope, but, alternatively, surface slope can be calculated from ice thickness. In this case the second term in (15) can be regarded as a correction term to the usual formula. In this term $\bar{\sigma}_x$, $\bar{\sigma}_y$ are the direct stresses in the horizontal and vertical directions, averaged over the ice thickness. Variations of σ_y with x are generally much smaller than the variations of σ_x. The correction term thus makes allowance for variations in longitudinal stress along the direction of flow. Robin thinks that these variations are important in many parts of ice sheets.

The correction term can be evaluated from measurements of longitudinal strain rate $\dot{\varepsilon}_x$, if two assumptions are made:

1. $\bar{\sigma}_x - \bar{\sigma}_y$ is large compared with $\bar{\tau}_{xy}$, the shear stress averaged over the ice thickness.
2. $\dot{\varepsilon}_x$ does not vary with depth.

Equation (15) was derived for a two-dimensional model in which all stresses involving z are zero. In this case, the first assumption implies that σ'_x, σ'_y are the only non-zero stress deviators. Moreover,

$$\sigma'_x = \tfrac{1}{2}(\sigma_x - \sigma_y)$$

and the flow law of ice gives

$$\dot{\varepsilon}_x = (\tfrac{1}{2})^n A(\bar{\sigma}_x - \bar{\sigma}_y)^n \tag{16}$$

The quantity A depends on ice temperature, which varies with depth. A value averaged over the depth must therefore be used. Values of $\bar{\sigma}_x - \bar{\sigma}_y$ and hence of the correction term in (15), can then be obtained from (16) using measurements of longitudinal strain rate along the profile.

Robin's data consisted of a profile of the Greenland ice sheet for 46 km along the estimated flow line south of Camp Century. The surface profile was obtained by altimetry; the bottom profile by radar. Strain rates were not measured; they had to be estimated from the continuity condition on the assumption that the ice sheet is in a steady state. The estimates of strain rate were based on measurements of ice thickness h and estimates of mass balance b and velocity u. The quantity A in (16) could be calculated because the temperature-depth profile at Camp Century has been measured (see Chapter 10). Robin was thus able to use (15) to calculate α_s at points along the profile, for comparison with observed surface slopes. He found that the calculated slopes were much closer to the observed values when the correction term in (15) was included than was the case when this term was omitted.

This type of analysis should be repeated at places where strain rates as well as profiles have been measured.

Instability of Ice Sheets

The theoretical profiles derived previously refer to an ice sheet in a steady state. Similarly the theory of glacier flow in Chapter 6 refers to a steady state except for a few results where this assumption was not necessary. In Chapter 11 we discuss what happens when a glacier is not in a steady state. More specifically, how the flow and thickness change in response to changes in mass balance. It is still implied, however, that the steady state profile is a stable one. In other words, if the mass balance changes slightly the glacier will, given time, attain a new steady state profile slightly different from the old one. This feature of the theory is ensured by the assumption that the equilibrium line always extends to a fixed distance from the head of the glacier (or from the centre of an ice sheet). Thus, if the glacier becomes longer, the total ablation will increase but the total accumulation will not change. This will make the terminus retreat towards its original position.

However, suppose we make the alternative assumption that the equilibrium line is always at a fixed elevation. In this case the steady state profile may be unstable. Bodvarsson (1955) first pointed this out and Weertman (1961c) has investigated the matter in detail. Figure 9.7 illustrates the situation. The steady

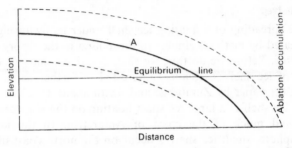

FIG. 9.7. Ice sheet with equilibrium line at fixed elevation. Profile A corresponds to a steady state. The other profiles may be unstable.

state profile, marked *A*, is that for which accumulation summed over the accumulation area equals ablation summed over the ablation area. If the ice sheet starts to grow, the accumulation area, and hence the total accumulation, will increase. The total accumulation might now be greater than the total ablation. In this case the ice sheet will continue to grow rather than shrink back towards the steady state profile. Similarly the total ablation of an ice sheet smaller than *A* may exceed the total accumulation. If the ice sheet starts to shrink it will continue to do so. In these circumstances the steady state profile is unstable.

We shall not give Weertman's mathematical analysis but merely state his conclusions. If a small ice sheet exceeds a certain critical width, it may be unstable and grow large, as a result of only a moderate increase in accumulation. Similarly a moderate decrease in accumulation (or increase in ablation), if maintained, might cause a large ice sheet to shrink away. The theoretical ice sheet is assumed in this case to lie on land which extends to infinity. This is not so in Antarctica where the sea provides a very high ablation rate at the edge of the ice sheet. The Greenland ice sheet is also limited by the sea, though to a lesser extent.

This instability is a theoretical idea: it has never been observed in practice. However, it might explain, or at least help to explain, the repeated growth and shrinkage of the ice sheets which covered much of Europe and North America during the Pleistocene.

Ice Shelves

The spreading of a floating ice shelf under its own weight can be treated by methods similar to those used in the theory of glacier flow. Before we do this, we shall describe some general features of ice shelves. Readers interested in further details could consult a paper by Zumberge and Swithinbank (1962).

An ice shelf is a large ice sheet floating on the sea. Ice shelves surround much of the coast of Antarctica. In the northern hemisphere, small ice shelves occur on the north coast of Ellesmere Island, in North Greenland, and in Franz Josef Land. Such ice is only called an ice shelf while it remains attached to the land or land ice. In the Arctic, detached parts of ice shelves are known as "ice islands". Several of these have served as scientific stations drifting in the Arctic Ocean. In the Antarctic they would be referred to as tabular bergs. The following data refer to the Antarctic.

The surface of an ice shelf is approximately horizontal, but may have gentle undulations. Crevasses are found mainly near the margins or in locally grounded areas. The landward margin can be identified by the start of the uphill slope of the inland ice sheet, and by "strand cracks" produced as the ice shelf rises and falls with the tide. The seaward margin is a vertical cliff, normally about 30 m high. (It is limited to this height by the plastic properties of ice, just as the depth of a crevasse is; see Chapter 6.)

Where an ice shelf is grounded over a considerable area, the surface is not horizontal but dome shaped. Such a region in the middle of an ice shelf is called an "ice rise". An ice rise may be up to 150 km long and its profile is the same as that of an ice cap, as discussed in an earlier section. Flow in an ice rise is radial and independent of flow in the surrounding ice shelf. Ice rises may in fact be a convenient size for detailed measurements, to test theoretical predictions about flow in an ice sheet. Figure 9.5 (page 154) shows an ice shelf and an ice rise.

The Ross Ice Shelf is the world's largest, with an area of 525×10^3 km^2. Its thickness varies from perhaps 700 m at the landward end to about 250 m at the ice front. Few measurements of flow velocity have been published. The average velocity is probably a few hundred metres per year, with a maximum of roughly 1 km y^{-1} at the seaward end. Such velocities result partly from the flow of the glaciers which feed the shelf and partly from the spreading of the shelf under its own weight as discussed in the next section. Temperatures at a depth of 10 m in the Ross Ice Shelf are in the range $-23°$ to $-28°$C. Measurements in other Antarctic ice shelves have ranged from about $-10°$ to $-30°$C. The lower surface is at the freezing point of sea water, about $-1.5°$C. The temperature distribution in an ice shelf is discussed in Chapter 10.

The important positive factors in the mass balance of Antarctic ice shelves are accumulation of snow at the surface plus the supply of ice from glaciers and from the main Antarctic ice sheet. In some cases ice may accumulate by freezing of sea water at the lower surface, a very difficult process to measure. Ice appears to melt from the underside of most of the Ross Ice Shelf, but there may be some accretion near the landward end.

The chief loss of mass is by calving of icebergs. Few measurements or detailed studies of this process have been made. The calving of ice is determined by oceanographic factors, such as waves, tsunamis, and tides, rather than by meteorological factors. This is one reason why, when the mass balance of the Antarctic ice sheet is calculated, the ice sheet is considered to end at the point where it starts to float: the ice shelves are excluded. Melting at the upper and lower surfaces and blowing of snow into the sea are other negative factors in the mass balance. However, there appears to be net accumulation at the surface of the great majority of Antarctic ice shelves.

The seaward edge of an ice shelf usually extends, more or less in a straight line, from one point of land to another. The extent of an ice shelf seems to depend largely on the protection afforded by land or grounded ice at its sides, and on shoals which can ground its outer margin. Thus the Antarctic ice shelves are unlikely to have ever extended beyond the outermost shoals surrounding the continent.

In the arctic, the ice shelf studied in most detail is the Ward Hunt Ice Shelf in northern Ellesmere Island. It is not fed by any glacier. In some years there is net accumulation at the surface; in others net ablation. Calving appears to be infrequent, but when ice does break off it is usually in a large mass. Calving during winter 1961–2 reduced the area of the shelf by almost half (Hattersley–Smith, 1963).

Flow of an Ice Shelf

A floating ice shelf will deform plastically under its own weight. The main difference between this process and the flow of a glacier is that the shear stress at the base of an ice shelf is zero. Thus the ice can deform even though its upper surface is horizontal. Deformation consists of uniform spreading, the rate of which we wish to calculate. The theory is due to Weertman (1957b).

Figure 9.8 shows the model. The thickness is assumed to be uniform, equal to h, and very much smaller than the length and width. A steady state is assumed, so that the thinning as the shelf

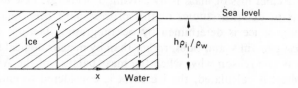

FIG. 9.8. Co-ordinate system: floating ice shelf.

spreads is supposed to be just compensated by accumulation. Thus h is constant in time as well as space. We consider the situation far from the edges. Take x-axis in the lower surface, y-axis vertical and positive upwards, z-axis normal to x and y. As most ice shelves are confined by land on either side, we can assume that there is no deformation in the z direction. Let ϱ_i, ϱ_w be the densities of ice and water, and g the acceleration due to gravity. For simplicity, ϱ_i is taken as constant.

The notation for stresses and strain rates is the same as in Chapter 6. It seems reasonable to assume that, far from the edges, all stresses are independent of x and z. The equilibrium equations for the stresses then reduce to

$$\partial \tau_{xy}/\partial y = 0$$
$$\partial \sigma_y/\partial y = -\varrho_i g$$
$$\partial \tau_{yz}/\partial y = 0$$

Boundary conditions are that shear stresses are zero at both upper and lower surfaces, and that σ_y is zero on the upper surface. (Atmospheric pressure is ignored.) A solution consistent with these conditions is

$$\tau_{xy} = \tau_{yz} = \tau_{zx} = 0 \tag{17}$$

$$\sigma_y = -\varrho_i g(h-y) \tag{18}$$

We have assumed that the strain rate $\dot{\varepsilon}_z$ is zero, and so, from the flow law of ice, the corresponding stress deviator σ_z' is also zero. Thus

$$\sigma_x' = -\sigma_y' = \tfrac{1}{2}(\sigma_x - \sigma_y)$$

Moreover, (17) shows that σ_x', σ_y' are the only non-zero stress deviators. Thus the flow law reduces to

$$\dot{\varepsilon}_x = (\tfrac{1}{2})^n A(\sigma_x - \sigma_y)^n$$

By (18) this can be written as

$$\sigma_x = 2A^{-1/n}\dot{\varepsilon}_x^{1/n} - \varrho_i g(h-y) \tag{19}$$

Now, at the end of the shelf, the force due to σ_x must just balance the horizontal force exerted by the water. Thus

$$\int\limits_0^h \sigma_x \, dy = - \int\limits_0^{h'} \varrho_w g(h'-y) \, dy$$

where

$$h' = h\varrho_i/\varrho_w$$

The conditions that $\dot{\varepsilon}_{xy}$ is zero and $\dot{\varepsilon}_x$, $\dot{\varepsilon}_y$ are independent of x, combined with the boundary condition that the vertical velocity v is zero at the base of the shelf, imply that $\dot{\varepsilon}_x$, $\dot{\varepsilon}_y$ are independent of y. Substitution from (19) gives

$$\dot{\varepsilon}_x = (\tfrac{1}{4} \varrho_i g h^2)^n (1 - \varrho_i/\varrho_w)^n (\int\limits_0^h A^{-1/n} \, dy)^{-n} \qquad (20)$$

This is the required strain rate in the shelf, far from the edge. (Note that, as temperature varies with depth in an ice shelf, we cannot assume that A is independent of y, as we assumed in the theory of glacier flow.) The strain rate is the same at all depths. As the expression is positive, the shelf can only spread: it cannot creep compressively. This agrees with intuition. It follows that, while the shelf can spread to maintain constant thickness in spite of accumulation, ablation must result in thinning. As n is about 3, the strain rate is proportional to the sixth power of the thickness.

Weertman also considered the case of a shelf not confined in the z direction. He found that the strain rate is increased by about 10 per cent. Any horizontal line on the shelf, whatever its orientation, will stretch by the same amount. This contrasts with the case treated above.

The strain rate calculated from (20) is close to the value measured by Schytt in the ice shelf in Queen Maud Land, Antarctica. This ice shelf is 185 m thick and the strain rate is about $2 \times 10^{-3} \text{ y}^{-1}$.

Other Applications of Flow Theory

The theory of the flow of glaciers and ice sheets has another potential application. This arises because, on a very long time scale (perhaps of the order of a million years), flow occurs in the earth's interior. The existence of convection currents in the earth's mantle is the subject of much discussion at the present time. In theoretical work, the material of the mantle is treated as a fluid of very high but constant viscosity. This was the basis of the theory of glacier flow until about 20 years ago, but the theory has now advanced far beyond that stage. As we have seen, a considerable body of theory has been built up on the foundations of a realistic flow law. The material of the earth's mantle does not flow in exactly the same way as ice. Nevertheless, application, to the problems of flow in the earth's interior, of some of the methods and results from glaciers might well be an improvement over current treatments. One or two steps have recently been taken in this direction.

For example, Weertman (1962b) considered what might happen if the material underlying the ocean had a slightly different density on one side of a continent than on the other side. If such a difference persisted down to depths of the order of 1000 km, it would result in a difference in depth between the two ocean basins. Weertman then applied his theory of the spreading of a floating ice shelf to show that the higher basin would expand and the lower one contract. This would cause movement of the intervening continent. Weertman proposed this as a possible mechanism of continental drift.

Again, Evison (1960) postulated that, over long periods of time, plastic flow under gravity takes place in a superficial layer of the earth's crust. Any increase in the average height of a continent by volcanic or orogenic activity will cause it to spread at the expense of the surrounding oceans. Evison showed that such a process could explain many observed features of the margins of continents. He further suggested that certain geological faults may form by shear fracture induced by plastic flow.

The postulates and results of such studies are not yet known, let alone accepted, by the majority of geophysicists. We mention them here merely to indicate that recent theoretical work on glacier flow may have an application wider than the immediate purpose for which it was developed.

CHAPTER 10

DISTRIBUTION OF TEMPERATURE IN GLACIERS AND ICE SHEETS

"This shows how much easier it is to be critical than to be correct."

DISRAELI.

Introduction

In 1931, members of Wegener's expedition measured temperatures in the central part of the Greenland ice sheet. They obtained the unexpected result that the temperature decreased with increasing depth. Most subsequent measurements in Greenland and Antarctica have shown this negative temperature gradient. Such observations have stimulated theoretical studies of the temperature distribution in a large ice sheet.

Many physical properties of ice are strongly dependent on temperature. The flow law is an example. The greater part of the mathematical theory of glacier flow is based on the simplifying assumption that the glacier is at the pressure melting temperature throughout. Thus it is important to know whether many glaciers are of this type. Again, sliding of a glacier on its bed can constitute a large part of the total movement. But the glacier can only slide when the lowest layers of ice are at the pressure melting point. The temperature at the base is important from the aspect of erosion: bedrock is protected when the glacier is frozen to it. Again, an instability in temperature at the glacier bed has been suggested as a cause of glacier surges. Such properties as the velocity of seismic waves, the DC resistivity, and the absorption of radio waves, on which depend techniques for measuring ice thickness, also vary with temperature. The temperature distribution thus deserves attention both for its intrinsic interest and for its relation to other processes in glaciers.

The temperature distribution results from the interaction of several factors. There are sources of heat at the glacier surface and at the base. Conduction, advection of ice, and flow of water may all transfer heat within the glacier. These factors vary in importance between different regions and even between different parts of the same glacier. Experimental data are still meagre, mainly because of the difficulty of deep drilling. And most theoretical studies have been based on rather drastic simplifying assumptions.

Before discussion of the general problem, we shall consider what determines the temperature in the upper layers of the glacier.

Ice Temperatures near the Glacier Surface

In a glacier there is an upper layer, some 15 m thick, in which the temperature varies in response to changes in air temperature at the surface during the year. In winter, the ice is warmer than the air and so heat is conducted upwards through the ice. It is convenient to regard this as propagation of a winter "cold wave" downwards into the ice. This part of the annual cycle can be treated by heat conduction theory.

The problem is one of heat conduction in a semi-infinite medium subject to an harmonic change of temperature at the surface. The equation of heat conduction reduces to

$$k\partial^2 T/\partial y^2 = \partial T/\partial t$$

with boundary condition,

$$T(0, t) = T_s \sin \omega t$$

Here T is temperature, t time, y distance below the surface measured positive downwards, k thermal diffusivity, T_s the amplitude and $\omega/2\pi$ the frequency of the temperature change at the surface.

The solution, when the transient term is neglected, is

$$T(y, t) = T_s \exp\left[-y(\omega/2k)^{1/2}\right] \sin\left[\omega t - y(\omega/2k)^{1/2}\right] \quad (1)$$

This solution shows:

1. The amplitude of the wave decreases as $\exp[-y(\omega/2k)^{1/2}]$. Thus, the higher the frequency, the more rapid the attenuation

with depth. In reality, the surface temperature during the year is a complicated function of time, but it can be expressed as an harmonic series. The higher harmonics are attenuated rapidly, and the temperature perturbation at depth is, to a good approximation, a wave of the fundamental frequency.

2. The velocity of propagation of the temperature minimum (the peak of the "cold wave") is $(2\omega k)^{1/2}$.

TABLE 10.1. CALCULATED TEMPERATURES (°C) AT VARIOUS DEPTHS PRODUCED BY A GIVEN SINE WAVE AT THE SURFACE

		Depth (m)			
		0	1	5	10
	0	−20	−17·2	−10·3	− 9·5
	1	−18·7	−17·3	−11·4	− 9·6
Time	2	−15	−15·5	−12·2	− 9·9
(months)	3	−10	−12·1	−12·4	−10·1
	4	− 5	− 8·3	−11·9	−10·4
	5	− 1·3	− 4·9	−10·9	−10·5
	6	0	− 2·8	− 9·7	−10·5
Time of minimum (months)		0	0·55	2·75	5·5

Substitution of numerical values ($k = 38 \text{ m}^2\text{y}^{-1}$, $\omega/2\pi = 1\text{y}^{-1}$) leads to the results in Table 10.1. This shows the temperature variation at different depths produced by a sinusoidal variation of surface temperature of amplitude 10 deg and period 1 year. For example, at a depth of 10 m, the minimum occurs $5\frac{1}{2}$ months after the minimum at the surface, and the amplitude of the temperature change is about 5 per cent of that at the surface. We may conclude that seasonal temperature changes cannot be detected below a depth of 15 or 20 m, and that at 10 m their amplitude is unlikely to exceed 1 deg. (The value of diffusivity for ice was used in this calculation. In snow, the amplitude of the wave at any given depth, and its velocity of propagation, would be somewhat smaller than the values given.)

Field measurements confirm these conclusions. For example, in the Antarctic ice sheet near Wilkes Station, Cameron and Bull (1962) found that the annual temperature wave had an amplitude of 0·85 deg at a depth of 10 m and 0·2 deg at 16 m. On Axel Heiberg Island in the Canadian Arctic, Müller (1963) found that seasonal temperature changes could be detected to a depth of 11 m near the highest point of one of the ice caps and to 16 m in the ablation area of a valley glacier.

Changes of surface temperature with periods much greater than one year, such as those due to climatic changes, may of course penetrate to greater depths than 20 m. These will be discussed later.

In most areas, the mechanism of heat transfer in the surface layers in summer differs from the winter mechanism. Except in the interiors of Greenland and Antarctica, there is enough heat in summer to cause melting at the surface. The meltwater percolates into the snow and, when it reaches a depth where the temperature is still below 0°C, it refreezes. Refreezing of 1 g of water produces enough latent heat to raise the temperature of 160 g of snow or firn by 1 deg. This process is very important in warming the layers near the surface. Figure 10.1 shows changes in temperature of the firn on Isachsen's Plateau in Spitsbergen, as measured by Sverdrup (1935a). The previous winter's cold wave was eliminated much more quickly than would have been possible by heat conduction alone. The temperature at a depth of 3 m changed by nearly 7 deg in less than a month.

The importance of meltwater penetration differs from one zone of a glacier to another. There is no meltwater in a dry snow zone. Some snow melts in the accumulation areas of the great majority of glaciers, and, until all the firn has been brought to the melting temperature, all the meltwater refreezes in the previous winter's snow cover or in the layers of preceding years. Thus a large amount of latent heat is available to raise the temperature of the glacier. In these zones meltwater penetration is a most important process.

12*

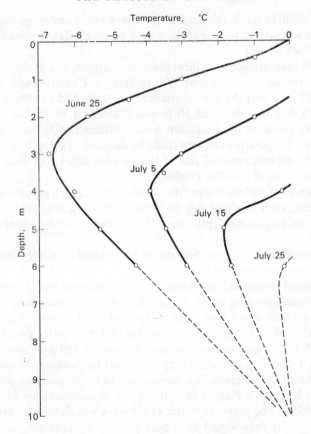

FIG. 10.1. Elimination of winter "cold wave" from firn. From Sverdrup (1935a).

In a zone of superimposed ice accumulation, the winter's snow
cover rests on impermeable ice. Formation of the superimposed
ice results in some warming, but most of the meltwater is lost by
run-off. In this zone the amount of warming by latent heat is small.
In the ablation area, the whole snow cover and some glacier ice
are lost during the summer. Thus the latent heat is lost and does
not warm the glacier.

It is often stated that the temperature measured at a depth of 10 or 15 m in a glacier is equal to the mean annual air temperature at that point. This is not true in general. If there is no melting, temperature changes throughout the year are propagated into the ice by heat conduction. In this case the theory given earlier for propagation of the winter cold wave can be applied to the whole year's temperature cycle. Equation (1) shows that, although the amplitude of seasonal temperature fluctuations decreases with depth, the mean temperature over a complete cycle is the same at all depths. Thus as a layer of firn is buried by the accumulation of subsequent years, its temperature eventually remains constant and equal to the mean annual air temperature at the surface. (We assume for the moment that the mean annual air temperature remains the same from year to year.) This is only true, however, in a region where the *maximum* air temperature is less than 0°C.

This argument breaks down in other cases. Refreezing of melt-water should make the firn temperature greater than the mean annual air temperature. On the other hand, the glacier surface temperature cannot rise above 0°C, even if the air temperature does. This tends to make the ice temperature less than mean annual air temperature. The winter snow cover also affects the ice temperature. Snow acts as a blanket which reduces the heat lost by the glacier during the winter. The ice temperature in the ablation area will thus be higher than it would be in the absence of snow. The situation is different in the accumulation area, because the snow there becomes part of the glacier. Other features that may produce local temperature variations are crevasses, which may collect large quantities of water in summer, and water channels within the ice.

How do these expectations compare with published data?

Table 10.2 shows firn temperatures and mean annual air temperatures at several stations in dry snow areas in Greenland and Antarctica. The two temperatures agree satisfactorily. The discrepancies can be explained by the fact that air temperatures were measured over one or a few years only. Their means may thus differ slightly from means over longer periods.

There are quite a few temperature measurements from regions where the firn is warmed by refreezing of meltwater; but nearby measurements of air temperature are usually lacking. However, Hughes and Seligman (1938) found that the temperature was 0°C at a depth of 30 m in the accumulation area of Aletsch Glacier in Switzerland. The mean annual air temperature at the nearby Jung-

TABLE 10.2. COMPARISON OF FIRN TEMPERATURE AND MEAN ANNUAL AIR TEMPERATURE IN DRY SNOW AREAS

Location	Lati-tude	Longi-tude	T°C firn	Depth (m)	T°C air	Reference
Northice Camp	78°04′N	38°29′W	−28	15	−30	Bull, 1956
Century	77°10′N	61°08′W	−24·0	10	−23·6	Weertman, 1968
Site 2	76°59′N	56°04′W	−24	8	−24·4	Diamond, 1960
Eismitte	71°11′N	39°56′W	−29	16·6	−30	Sorge, 1933
Byrd Station	80°S	120°W	−28	15	−29	Gow, 1963b
South Pole	90°S		−51	10	−51	Sharp, 1960

fraujoch research station is −7°C. Lliboutry (1963) also measured a temperature of 0°C to a depth of 30 m in the Vallée Blanche in France. The mean annual air temperature there is −8°C.

Another interesting comparison is between temperatures at different points in the same glacier, as in Table 10.3. Because air temperature decreases with increase of elevation one might expect temperatures to be lower in the accumulation area than in the ablation area. Table 10.3 shows that this is not always the case. As before, refreezing of meltwater in the firn provides the explanation.

If summers were to become colder, part of a glacier might be converted from an ablation area, or an area of superimposed ice accumulation, into an area of firn accumulation. In this case its near-surface temperature would increase. Thus a decrease in air temperature would have produced an increase in glacier temperature. This illustrates how complicated the relation between climate and glaciers may be.

TABLE 10.3. TEMPERATURES AT DIFFERENT POINTS IN SAME GLACIER

Glacier	Area	T°C	Depth (m)	Reference
White Glacier, Axel Heiberg Island, Canada	firn accumulation near equilibrium line ablation	− 9·5 −16 −13	8 8 8	Müller, 1963
Jackson Ice Cap, Franz Josef Land, U.S.S.R.	firn accumulation ice accumulation ablation	− 3 − 9 − 6 to −10·5*	20 20 20	Krenke, 1963
Vestfonna Ice Cap, N.E. Land, Spitsbergen	accumulation ablation	− 3 − 7 to −10*	14 10	Schytt, 1964

* Temperatures measured at various elevations.

Temperate Glaciers

Related to topics discussed in the previous section is the question of so-called temperate glaciers. A "temperate" glacier, as usually defined, is one which is at the pressure melting temperature throughout, except for seasonal changes near the surface. Glaciers which are not temperate can be classified as "cold". Temperate glaciers are encountered frequently in the literature: how widespread they are in nature remains uncertain. It is sometimes assumed that most, if not all, glaciers outside the polar regions are temperate. But there is little direct evidence on this point.

In fact it seems unlikely that all the ice in any glacier is always exactly at the melting point. The pressure on any element of ice changes as snow collects on the surface in the winter and as snow and ice melt in the summer. Ice, originally at the pressure melting point, will not remain there when the pressure is reduced. Again, pressure changes are likely to result in small amounts of melting and refreezing within the glacier. Release and absorption of latent heat in these processes can cause temperature changes in the adjacent ice. Strain-work also generates heat within the ice and conduction is possible along the pressure melting gradient. Again, a layer of cold firn may form in the accumulation area following one or a series of abnormally cold summers. Such a layer will eventually be brought to the melting temperature by conduction of heat from warmer layers above and below it. But heat conduction in ice is a slow process.

A necessary condition for a glacier to be temperate is that the entire snow cover in the accumulation area attain a temperature of 0°C every summer. This is not a sufficient condition. We have seen that, in the accumulation area, penetration of meltwater can raise the temperature of the firn to 0°C, even in regions where the mean annual air temperature is well below this value. In the ablation area, however, while water can penetrate the glacier in small cracks, crevasses, and moulins, the bulk of the ice is impermeable to water. Thus the winter cold wave can only be eliminated by conduction, a much less effective process than refreezing of meltwater. In some cases, conduction may be inadequate. Temperate ice, formed in the accumulation area, will then be cooled below 0°C as it approaches the surface in the ablation area. We might therefore expect to find glaciers which are temperate in the accumulation area but cold, at least in their upper layers, in the ablation area. Loewe (1966) has pointed out that the Sukkertoppen Ice Cap in West Greenland is in this category.

Two factors counteract this tendency. First, the winter snow reduces the loss of heat from the underlying ice. Second, part of the ice penetrated by the cold wave will be removed by ablation the following summer. Thus the most likely place to find temperate glaciers is one where heavy winter snowfalls are followed by intense summer melting that is, a region with a maritime temperate climate. Shumskiy and others (1964) state that only in moist maritime climates are the glaciers temperate: but they quote no measurements.

Classifications such as "temperate" or "cold" should be restricted to specified areas of a glacier: one should not try to include the whole glacier in a single category.

Certain Russian scientists have recently used a different approach to this problem. They have redefined a temperate glacier as one in which, below the depth of seasonal variations, all the ice and firn is at, or within 1 deg of, the melting point.

Few temperature measurements have been made at depth in ice near the melting point. To the normal problems of deep drilling is added the fact that drilling may affect the temperature by introducing meltwater and by changing the pressure in the ice.

In the European Alps in the early 1900's Blümcke and Hess measured temperatures down to a depth of 148 m in the ablation area of Hintereisferner. The glacier appeared to be temperate there. However, the ice temperature was probably affected by water used in the drilling. The measurements of Hughes and Seligman (1938) and of Lliboutry (1963), quoted previously, showed that the accumulation areas of these glaciers are temperate.

In the North Tien Shan Mountains, U.S.S.R. (latitude 43°N), Vilesov (1961) measured temperatures at a point about 0·5 km from the terminus of Central Tuyuksu Glacier. Temperatures ranged from $-2·5°C$ at a depth of 10 m to $-0·7°C$ at the base of the glacier (52 m). Thus the glacier is not temperate. This region has a continental type of climate.

In the northwestern U.S.A., Blue Glacier has been shown to be temperate by measurements in the accumulation area (LaChapelle, 1961). In the ablation area, however, Shreve (1961) found that ice formed inside cased boreholes. This suggests that the glacier may not be temperate in the ablation area. Blue Glacier is within 75 km of the Pacific Ocean in latitude 48°N. The climate is mild and extremely wet, conditions under which glaciers might be expected to be temperate. Again, Mathews (1964) measured temperatures in the range $-1·9°$ to $-2·5°C$ in a tunnel in bedrock under South Leduc Glacier. This glacier is in western Canada in latitude 56°N, some 100 km from the coast. Further inland, in the more continental climate of the Canadian Rocky Mountains, there is some indirect evidence that Saskatchewan and Athabasca Glaciers (latitude 52°N) are not truly temperate in their ablation areas. On Saskatchewan Glacier, Meier (1960) encountered difficulties in thermal drilling which suggested that the ice was below the melting point. On Athabasca Glacier, Savage and Paterson (1963) found that ice formed in cased boreholes in a few days, at depths well below the limit of the winter cold wave.

Some information about ice temperature may be obtained by indirect means. For example, if ablation stakes are still frozen in their holes at the end of the ablation season, the glacier is not strictly temperate. Again, if streams emerge from underneath the terminus, at least the base of the glacier is at the melting point. In cold glaciers, streams do not descend to the bed; they discharge through tunnels or deep gorges high up on the terminus or sides of the glacier. Some information can also be obtained from the velocity of compressional seismic waves. Velocities in the range 3600 to 3660 m sec^{-1} indicate that the ice is probably near the melting point. Velocity increases as temperature decreases (Robin, 1958).

General Equation of Heat Transfer

We now turn to the question of the temperature distribution in a large ice sheet. If we drill a hole through the ice sheet, how would we expect the temperature to vary with depth? The answer depends on conditions at the surface and the base, and on how heat is transferred within the ice sheet. The temperature at the surface is determined by the climate; it may vary with time. At the base there is a constant influx of geothermal heat, and also some frictional heat if the ice is sliding over its bed. Differential movement generates heat within the ice sheet, and heat is transferred from point to point by both thermal conduction and ice movement. In the accumulation area for example, the ice movement vectors are inclined slightly downwards relative to the surface. Thus as we drill deeper we encounter ice which originated as snow at progressively higher elevations on the surface. Thus the ice should become progressively colder with increase of depth. Each ice layer will not retain its original temperature indefinitely however, because conduction will transfer heat between adjacent layers. We shall now treat the problem mathematically.

The base of the ice sheet is assumed to be horizontal. We take the origin on the base at the centre of the ice sheet, the x-axis horizontal and in the direction of ice flow, the y-axis vertical, positive upwards, and the z-axis so as to make the system right-handed. This coordinate system is fixed in space.

The general equation of heat transfer in a moving medium can be written:

$$DT/Dt - k\nabla^2 T = H/\varrho c \qquad (2)$$

This equation is derived by Carslaw and Jaeger (1959, p. 13). Here T denotes temperature, t time, k thermal diffusivity (assumed constant), ϱ density, c specific heat, and H the internal heat generated per unit volume and time. Also,

$$DT/Dt = \partial T/\partial t + u\,\partial T/\partial x + v\,\partial T/\partial y + \omega\,\partial T/\partial z$$

where u, v, w are the components of ice velocity. In the present case,

$$2JH = (\dot{\varepsilon}_x \sigma'_x + \dot{\varepsilon}_y \sigma'_y + \dot{\varepsilon}_z \sigma'_z + 2\dot{\varepsilon}_{xy}\tau_{xy} + 2\dot{\varepsilon}_{xz}\tau_{xz} + 2\dot{\varepsilon}_{yz}\tau_{yz}) \qquad (3)$$

where the $\dot{\varepsilon}$ are components of strain rate and the σ', τ are stress deviators. Strain rates and stress deviators are related by the flow law, which depends on temperature (see Chapter 6). The quantity J is the mechanical equivalent of heat.

Certain simplifications can be made:

1. The x-axis is in the direction of flow. Thus $w = 0$.
2. We assume that k is a constant. The value of k for firn and ice varies by only 5 per cent for densities of 0.6 g cm^{-3} or greater. The assumption is therefore reasonable except for the top 20 or 30 m of a polar ice sheet.
3. In an ice sheet, temperature gradients in the horizontal directions are small compared with the vertical gradient. Thus $\partial^2 T/\partial x^2$ and $\partial^2 T/\partial z^2$ can be neglected and $\nabla^2 T = \partial^2 T/\partial y^2$.
4. In the present two-dimensional model of an ice sheet, all strain rates which involve z are zero. In addition, the internal heating due to $\dot{\varepsilon}_x$, $\dot{\varepsilon}_y$ is usually assumed to be small compared with that due to $\dot{\varepsilon}_{xy}$. This is certainly true near the base, where the heating is greatest. Thus $H = \dot{\varepsilon}_{xy}\tau_{xy}/J$.

Equation (2) thus becomes

$$\partial T/\partial t = k\, \partial^2 T/\partial y^2 - u\, \partial T/\partial x - v\, \partial T/\partial y + \dot{\varepsilon}_{xy}\tau_{xy}/J\varrho c \qquad (4)$$

The boundary conditions are:

1. T_s, the surface temperature, is a specified function of position and time.
2. At $y = 0$, $(\partial T/\partial y)_b = -G/K$

where G is the geothermal heat flux and K is the thermal conductivity of ice. We assume for the moment that the basal ice is below the pressure melting point. If it is not, the second boundary condition may not apply.

To obtain an analytical solution of equation (4), further simplifications are necessary. These will be discussed in subsequent sections.

Steady State Solution

The simplest solution of equation (4) is a steady state solution, obtained by taking $\partial T/\partial t = 0$. In such a solution, none of the quantities varies with time: the temperature profile along a given vertical line (fixed in space) is assumed to remain unchanged as the ice flows past. Robin (1955) obtained such a solution applicable to the central area of an ice sheet. He made the following assumptions in addition to those listed previously.

1. The horizontal advection term $u\partial T/\partial x$ is negligible. This should be the case near the centre of an ice sheet. The horizontal velocity there is small and, as the surface is almost horizontal, the surface temperature should vary very little with distance x.

2. The internal heat can be treated as a flux, additional to the geothermal flux, at the base of the ice sheet. In this case, the heat generated within the ice is taken to be zero in equation (4). This is a reasonable approximation for most purposes because most of the shearing in an ice sheet occurs near its base (see Chapter 9). The additional flux is equal to a normal geothermal flux when the ice velocity is about 20 m y $^{-1}$.

3. To obtain a solution, the vertical velocity v must be expressed as a function of position. At the surface v must balance the accu-

mulation of snow, otherwise the ice thickness would change with time, contrary to the assumed steady state. At the base v must be zero as it is assumed that no ice is melted there. We therefore take $v = -by/h$ where h is ice thickness and b is net mass balance expressed as thickness of ice (per year). The velocity v is assumed to have the same value for all x. Thus b and h are constants. This implies that the surface is horizontal, as is the case at the centre of an ice sheet. (Because ice is incompressible, $\partial u/\partial x = -\partial v/\partial y = b/h$. The relation assumed for y is thus consistent with the assumption, discussed in Chapter 6, that the longitudinal strain rate is the same at all depths.)

Equation (4) now becomes

$$k\, \partial^2 T/\partial y^2 + (by/h)\, \partial T/\partial y = 0 \tag{5}$$

The boundary conditions are

$$T_s = \text{constant}$$
$$(\partial T/\partial y)_b = \text{constant}$$

One integration gives

$$\partial T/\partial y = (\partial T/\partial y)_b \exp(-y^2/l^2) \tag{6}$$

where $l = (2kh/b)^{1/2}$

A second integration gives

$$T - T_b = (\partial T/\partial y)_b \int_0^y \exp(-y^2/l^2)\, dy \tag{7}$$

This can also be written

$$T - T_s = \tfrac{1}{2}\pi^{1/2}\, l\, (\partial T/\partial y)_b\, [\text{erf}(y/l) - \text{erf}(h/l)] \tag{8}$$

where $\text{erf}\, z = 2\pi^{-1/2} \int_0^z \exp(-Y^2)\, dY$

This is Robin's solution. Figure 10.2 shows the corresponding temperature distribution in an ice sheet 2500 m thick, for various values of mass balance. A value of 2·3 deg per 100 m was taken for

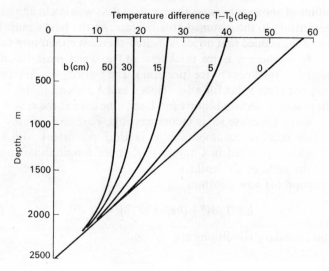

FIG. 10.2. Steady state temperature distribution in an ice sheet 2500 m thick, for various values of net mass balance (b cm of ice).

$(\partial T/\partial y)_b$. This gradient corresponds to a normal value of geothermal heat flux. The curves will apply to other values of heat flux if the temperature scale is adjusted so that $(T_s - T_b)/h$ is equal to $(\partial T/\partial y)_b$. If the surface temperature and mass balance are known, these curves may be used to determine whether the base of an ice sheet is at the pressure melting point. For example, at Byrd Station in Antarctica, h is roughly 2500 m and b is about 15 cm. The expected temperature difference between top and bottom is 25·5 deg. As T_s at Byrd Station is $-28°C$. We should expect the base to be just below the pressure melting temperature ($-1·6°C$), provided that the assumptions (a steady state, negligible horizontal velocity and surface slope, normal geothermal heat flux) are valid.

Robin's solution has to be modified slightly when the base is at the pressure melting point. Let b' be the thickness of ice melted from the base in unit time. The equation for the vertical velocity becomes

$$v = -b' - by/h$$

The solution is now

$$T - T_b = (\partial T/\partial y)_b \int_0^y \exp\left[-k^{-1}\left(by^2/2h + b'y\right)\right] dy$$

Weertman (1961b) and Zotikov (1963) have obtained this solution. Zotikov's paper contains temperature–depth curves calculated from this equation for various values of b and b'. Both authors give graphs of the critical thickness at which the base of the ice reaches the pressure melting point, for various values of the other parameters. Zotikov estimates, on the basis of his graphs, that the basal ice may reach the melting point over about half the area of the Antarctic ice sheet.

Temperatures near the Base of an Ice Sheet

Lliboutry (1964, p. 413; 1966) has discussed the different thermal conditions which may exist in the basal layers of an ice sheet.

Equation (7), with $y = h$, gives

$$T_s - T_b = (\partial T/\partial y)_b \int_0^h \exp\left(-y^2/l^2\right) dy \qquad (9)$$

The temperature gradient at the base is controlled by the geothermal heat flux: it cannot be positive. The integral on the right-hand side of equation (9) is always positive: its value depends mainly on ice thickness h, but also on the mass balance. The basal temperature T_b must be 0°C or below. Thus, because the right-hand side of the equation is not positive, T_s must be negative.

If T_s is sufficiently low, T_b will be below the pressure melting point. In this case all the geothermal heat enters the ice. If T_s increases, T_b will increase as well. At some critical value of T_s, T_b will reach the melting point. For values of T_s above this critical value, the temperature gradient through the ice sheet is insufficient to carry off all the geothermal heat. As T_s increases above the critical value, a diminishing fraction of the geothermal heat enters the ice, and $(\partial T/\partial y)_b$ decreases. The rest of the heat is used in melting ice at the base; but melting is confined to a very thin layer. (Recall that equations (7) and (9) no longer apply when the base is at the melting point.)

With further increase of T_s, a second critical value will be reached. At this value, no geothermal heat enters the ice and the temperature gradient in the basal ice becomes zero. Lliboutry believes that, in these circumstances, a layer of ice at least several metres thick may reach the melting point.

Now consider a region of an ice sheet in which T_s is constant and sufficiently low so that T_b is below the melting point. Suppose that in the downstream direction the ice flows into a bedrock valley so that the ice thickness increases. Equation (9) shows that an increase in h results in an increase in T_b if T_s remains constant. If thickening is sufficient, a point will be reached at which T_b attains the melting temperature. If the ice sheet continues to increase in thickness downstream from this point, there may be a point at which the second critical limit is reached with the formation of a layer of ice of finite thickness at the melting point. As a result of compressing flow, this layer will grow progressively thicker downstream, as long as the total ice thickness continues to increase.

Lliboutry has therefore suggested that temperate layers of ice may occur at the base of a large ice sheet in places where the ice flows over hollows and valleys in the bedrock.

Negative Temperature Gradients in Polar Ice Sheets

Very few temperature measurements had been made in polar ice sheets when Robin (1955) published his steady state solution, equation (7). The French Polar Expeditions had, however, confirmed the negative temperature gradient (decrease of temperature with increase of depth) found by Wegener's Expedition (Sorge, 1933) in the near-surface layers in the central part of the Greenland ice sheet. At "Station Centrale" the negative gradient extended to a depth of 120 m. Its average value over the range 20 to 120 m was -0.8 deg per 100 m. At "Camp 6", some 80 km from the western margin of the ice sheet, the gradient was -3.4 deg per 100 m (Holtzscherer and Bauer, 1954). Most subsequent measurements in Greenland and Antarctica have also shown negative temperature gradients extending, in some cases, to depths of several hundred metres. For example, gradients were negative throughout a 411 m borehole at Site 2, Greenland (Hansen and Landauer, 1958) and a 309 m borehole at Byrd Station, Antarctica (Gow, 1963). The ice at these two stations is between 2000 and 2500 m thick. On the other hand, in ice 540 m thick near Mirny Station, Antarctica, Bogoslovski (1958) found that the temperature reached a minimum at 150 m below the surface and increased with further increase in depth. An increase of temperature is expected, at least in the deeper layers, because of geothermal and other sources of heat at the base of the ice sheet.

The curves in Fig. 10.2 (page 182) do not, however, have negative gradients anywhere. The observations are thus inconsistent with Robin's steady state solution. Robin (1955) did, however, suggest an explanation: ice at depth in a borehole has flowed from higher parts of the ice sheet where it was laid down as snow at the lower air temperatures prevailing there. In other words, the negative gradient results from the horizontal advection term $u(\partial T/\partial x)$ in equation (4). (This term should be very small near the centre of the ice sheet, which is the region where the steady state solution applies.) Robin used a simple geometrical argument to derive a formula for the negative temperature gradient. The derivation is based on the assumption that all terms in the heat transfer equation, including the conduction term, are negligible compared with the horizontal advection term. At best, this assumption will only be valid for layers within a few hundred metres of the surface. At greater depths, conduction of geothermal heat cannot be ignored.

In Fig. 10.3, the coordinate y is measured vertically, positive downwards, with origin at P_1. The horizontal surface velocity is u. The surface slope is α. The thickness added to the surface in one year is b. The decrease of air temperature with unit increase of elevation is λ; its value is expected to be in the range 0·6 to 1·4 deg per 100 m.

After 1 year, ice which was on the surface at P_1 is buried to a depth b and has moved to a point P_1' below P_2. If T_1, T_2 are the mean annual air temperatures at P_1 and P_2, the temperature

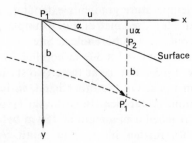

FIG. 10.3. Derivation of formula for negative temperature gradient.
In one year a point at P_1 moves to P_1' and an ice layer of thickness b
accumulates on the surface.

gradient over the depth P_2P_1' is $(T_1-T_2)/b$. But the difference in
y coordinates of P_1 and P_2 is $u\alpha$ approximately. Therefore

$$T_2-T_1 = u\alpha\lambda$$

It follows that

$$(\partial T/\partial y)_s = -u\alpha\lambda/b \qquad (10)$$

Both u and α increase with distance from the centre of an ice
sheet. Thus the negative temperature gradient should get larger
as one moves away from the centre. The French observations,
quoted above, show this trend.

A change in climate might also produce a negative temperature
gradient. This is how Sorge (1933) explained the original observations in central Greenland. If the mean air temperature increased over the years when the upper layers of the ice sheet were
being deposited as snow, each layer would be warmer than the
one below it. This process would explain a negative gradient
provided that two conditions are met. First, each layer retains
its original temperature. Thus heat conduction must be neglected.
Second, each ice particle remains vertically below the point
where it was deposited on the surface. Otherwise advection of ice,
laid down elsewhere at a different temperature, would affect the
temperature profile. Thus the explanation in terms of climatic
change is based on the assumption that the vertical advection
term is dominant in the equation of heat transfer.

In theory at least, one can choose between the two explanations, in any particular case, by calculating a temperature gradient from equation (10). If this does not agree with the measured gradient, one can postulate a climatic change to account for the difference. Measurement of surface velocity is difficult in a large ice sheet, but an estimate may be used in equation (10). Robin analysed the French observations in Greenland in this way. He concluded that horizontal advection of ice could explain the greater part of the negative gradient at Camp 6. On the other hand, climatic warming appeared to be the important factor at Station Centrale. In Antarctica, Mellor (1960) measured temperatures down to depths of 30 or 40 m in the ice sheet in MacRobertson Land. He used equation (10) to calculate ice velocities from the observed negative gradients, and obtained values which seemed unreasonably high. This suggested that the climate had recently become warmer in that area also.

Transient Temperature Distributions

A steady state solution gives the temperature distribution attained when factors such as surface temperature, mass balance, and ice thickness remain constant for a long time. For the Greenland and Antarctic ice sheets "a long time" means several thousand years: conditions are not expected to remain unchanged over such a period. Thus one wants to solve the equation of heat transfer with $\partial T/\partial t$ not zero. For an ice sheet of finite thickness the equation has to be solved numerically. Jenssen and Radok (1963) have used a computer for this. They start from the following assumptions:

1. The base of the ice sheet is horizontal and the surface is a parabola. (The theoretical shape if ice were perfectly plastic; see Chapter 9.)

2. At any point the horizontal velocity u is the same at all depths, but varies with distance from the edge of the ice sheet.

3. The vertical velocity v varies linearly with depth.

4. The net mass balance is constant in space and time.

5. The surface temperature increases 1 deg for each 100 m decrease of elevation.

13*

6. At the base, there is a constant geothermal heat flux plus an amount of frictional heat which depends on the velocity u.

7. The initial temperature distribution is that for a steady state, with no frictional heat at the base.

Jenssen and Radok used a coordinate system moving with velocity u. The term $u\, \partial T/\partial x$ could thus be omitted from the equation of heat transfer. However, they inserted a term involving $\partial k/\partial y$ to allow for the variation of thermal diffusivity with depth in the upper layers of the ice sheet.

To study conditions in the central part of the Antarctic ice sheet, the distance from the centre to the edge was taken as 3000 km and the maximum ice thickness as 3000 m. Consider a column of ice near the centre where the thickness is 2950 m and the velocity u is assumed to be 20 m y^{-1}. As this column of ice flows towards the edge, the elevation of its surface decreases in accordance with the parabolic profile and so its surface temperature increases. Because the thickness of the column (in the vertical direction) is decreasing and there is accumulation at the surface, continuity considerations show that the velocity u must increase with time. Thus, the frictional heat at the base also increases. If the base reaches the pressure melting temperature, ice will be melted there.

Jenssen and Radok present their results as graphs of temperature versus depth in the column of ice, at different times and for different values of mass balance. The curves show that the basal ice is gradually warmed up to the melting point and that a negative temperature gradient gradually develops in the upper layers. These curves are valuable as indications of general trends. One would hardly expect a temperature profile measured at some point in Antarctica to agree closely with any of the curves, because the model has certain defects. For instance, the parabolic profile chosen by Jenssen and Radok corresponds to a yield stress of about 0.25 bar. A value of 1 bar is more appropriate for ice. Also, Jenssen and Radok take an initial velocity of 20 m y^{-1} at a point, 100 km from the centre of the ice sheet, where the ice is 2950 m thick. Conservation of mass then requires a mass balance of 59 cm y^{-1}. In fact, Jenssen and Radok use values of 5, 20 and 80 cm y $^{-1}$. Again, the initial temperature distribution is taken to be Robin's steady state distribution with only a geothermal heat flux at the base. The initial velocity is taken as 20 m y $^{-1}$, however, and this would double the heat flux.

Wexler (1959) and Tien (1960) have studied how temperature in an ice sheet changes during its growth. In both analyses, the ice sheet is taken to be stagnant so that the equation of heat transfer reduces to

$$\partial T/\partial t = k \, \partial^2 T/\partial y^2$$

Tien considers an ice sheet growing from zero thickness at a constant rate. There is a constant geothermal heat flux at the base and it is assumed that none of this heat escapes from the surface. The surface temperature varies linearly with time, to represent climatic change. On Wexler's model, the ice sheet is semi-infinite with a constant geothermal heat flux at its base. Initially, temperature increases linearly with distance above the base.

Both Tien and Wexler obtain analytical solutions and then substitute numerical values appropriate to the ice sheet at Byrd Station, Antarctica. In Tien's curves, the temperature of the lower layers increases steadily with time. A negative temperature gradient develops in the upper layers after the ice sheet has been growing for about 5000 years. After another 5000 years, the negative gradient extends through about half the thickness of the ice sheet. Wexler's curves resemble those of Tien.

Temperature Profile through the Greenland Ice Sheet

The drilling of a borehole through the Greenland ice sheet, completed in 1966, was a major step forward in our knowledge of the temperature distribution. Previous drillings in both Greenland and Antarctica had penetrated to depths of only a few hundred metres. This borehole is at Camp Century (latitude 77°10′N, longitude 61°08′ W), some 100 km from the western margin of the ice sheet. The ice there is 1387 m thick.

Figure 10.4 shows the temperature profile as measured by Hansen (Hansen and Langway, 1966). Temperature decreases from $-24 \cdot 0°C$ at a depth of 10 m to a minimum of $-24 \cdot 6°C$ at 154 m. Below this, temperature increases and reaches $-13 \cdot 0°C$ at the base of the ice. The temperature gradient in the lowest 300 m is constant: its value corresponds to a geothermal heat flux of $1 \cdot 00 \times 10^{-6}$ cal cm^{-2} sec^{-1}. This is about 70 per cent of the world-wide average value.

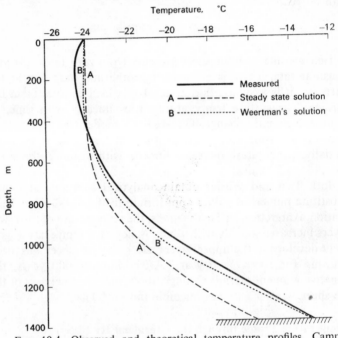

FIG. 10.4. Observed and theoretical temperature profiles, Camp Century, Greenland. From Weertman (1968).

Weertman (1968) has studied the profile in detail. We shall now summarize his analysis.

Figure 10.4 also shows Robin's steady state solution, equation (8), for the measured values of ice thickness, basal temperature gradient, and mass balance. This curve does not have a negative gradient in the upper layers and, at the base, the calculated temperature is 2·7 deg below that observed. Weertman examined how the steady state solution had to be modified to fit the observations satisfactorily. His analysis is not a new solution to the general problem; it is an adaptation of the steady state solution to the particular conditions at Camp Century.

It will be recalled that Robin's steady state solution is the solution of the equation

$$k \, \partial^2 T/\partial y^2 - v \, \partial T/\partial y = 0 \tag{5}$$

with $v = -by/h$. We have also seen that a negative temperature gradient can result from the horizontal advection of ice that is, from the term $u(\partial T/\partial x)$ in equation (4). One might expect this term to be important at Camp Century, which is far from the central ridge of the ice sheet. On the other hand, the velocity u is only 3·3 m y $^{-1}$. Another possible modification is to take account of the heat generated in the ice by the shear strain, that is, $\dot{\varepsilon}_{xy}\tau_{xy}/J$. (In Robin's solution this heat is treated as a flux at the base and added to the geothermal flux.) Most of this heat is generated in the basal layers. A solution which takes this heat into account will give a higher temperature for these layers than will a solution which ignores it. The equation to be solved is thus

$$k \, \partial^2 T/\partial y^2 - u \, \partial T/\partial x - v \, \partial T/\partial y + \dot{\varepsilon}_{xy}\tau_{xy}/J\varrho c = 0 \tag{11}$$

An analytical solution is possible if the two new terms can be expressed as simple functions of y. These terms involve the quantities u, $\dot{\varepsilon}_{xy} (= \frac{1}{2} \, \partial u/\partial y)$, τ_{xy}, $\partial T/\partial x$. The shear stress is obtained from equation (12′) of Chapter 6, namely

$$\tau_{xy} = \varrho g \, (h-y) \sin \alpha$$

Because the temperature is known at each depth, $\dot{\varepsilon}_{xy}$ can be obtained from the corresponding value of τ_{xy} by the flow law of ice. Numerical integration of the curve of $\dot{\varepsilon}_{xy}$ against y then gives u as a function of y. To obtain $\partial T/\partial x$ at each depth, Weertman differentiated Robin's steady state solution with respect to x. From this he derived an approximate relation for $\partial T/\partial x$ in terms of its value at the surface, the temperature at each depth, and the quantities $\partial h/\partial x$ and $\partial b/\partial x$. All these are known. Weertman found that the quantity $(\dot{\varepsilon}_{xy}\, \tau_{xy}/J\varrho c) - u\, \partial T/\partial x$ could be represented approximately by a constant in the upper 1000 m of the profile and by a linear function of y in the lower 400 m. Equation (11) can then be solved analytically. This is another steady state solution.

This new solution gives a temperature–depth curve with a negative gradient near the surface. However, the minimum temperature is only 0·14 deg below the surface temperature, compared with an observed difference of 0·6 deg. Moreover, predicted and observed basal temperatures differ by 2·0 deg.

Weertman next considered the possibility that, in the past, values of mass balance, velocity, or surface temperature may have differed from their present values. Repetition of the calculations with a different value of velocity does not reduce the discrepancy between calculated and observed temperatures. However, if a mass balance of 22·4 cm y $^{-1}$ is used instead of the present value of 35 cm y $^{-1}$, the resulting temperature–depth curve (curve B in Fig. 10.4) is always within 0·5 deg of the observed curve.

The only serious discrepancy between curve B and the observations is in the upper 300 m. In curve B, the minimum temperature is 0·1 deg less than the surface temperature: the actual difference is 0·6 deg. The minimum temperature occurs at a depth of about 150 m. This thickness of ice would take nearly 1000 years to accumulate if the mass balance has the value used in the calculations. The discrepancy in minimum temperatures would be explained if, 1000 years ago, the surface temperature was 0·5 deg colder than it is now. This simple argument rests on the assumption that each layer of ice still has the same temperature as when it was deposited. This is not strictly true: heat conduction will have modified these temperatures.

Langway's (1967) analysis of a 411 m core from Site 2 provides some information on climatic changes during the past 1000 years. Site 2 is about 130 km east of Camp Century. Langway found no evidence of the trends postulated by Weertman. Mass balance shows no consistent trend over this period; its value is almost the same now as it was 1000 years ago. Temperatures decreased slowly from the 10th to the 18th century, and increased quite rapidly thereafter. Present temperature is about the same as it was 1000 years ago. Langway's temperature analysis is, however, based on signs of melting at different depths in the core. Such signs are related to maximum summer temperature rather than to mean annual temperature.

Weertman's curves are based on steady state solutions, except for the postulated increase in temperature during the last 1000 years. The age of the basal ice can be estimated from the assumed accumulation rate, provided one allows for the thinning of the layers by vertical compression. The estimated age is roughly 15,000 years. A steady state solution rests on the premise that ice thickness, velocity, mass balance, and surface temperature have remained constant during this period. The past 15,000 years have seen the final stages of continental ice sheets in Europe and North America, followed by a "Climatic Optimum" in which the climate was warmer than it is now. There must surely have been considerable changes in Greenland during this time. A steady state model would hardly be expected to apply to this case. There seems a need for further study, both of the Camp Century profile and of the general subject of the temperature distribution in a large ice sheet.

Ice Shelves

The temperature distribution in a floating ice shelf has also been studied. We shall only mention this work briefly.

As before, the equation of heat transfer has to be solved. The main difference is in the boundary condition at the base. For an ice shelf, the condition is that the temperature at the base is constant and equal to the freezing point of sea water. The surface temperature can be taken as constant or as a linear function of time to represent climatic change. One must allow for accumulation or ablation at the surface and for melting of ice or accumulation by freezing of sea water at the base. The vertical ice velocity v is assumed to be a linear function of depth. Much of the ice in Antarctic ice shelves originates on land and is carried across the coastline by flow. The initial temperature distribution, which has to be assumed, should be chosen so as to be consistent with this fact.

Wexler (1960, 1961) and Crary (1960) have obtained analytical solutions of the heat transfer equation in a few special cases such as a steady state, a very thick ice shelf, no melting or accumulation at one or both surfaces, accumulation at the surface balanced by melting at the base. Jenssen and Radok (1961) have used a computer to obtain numerical solutions for more complex conditions. The temperature distribution in the Ross Ice Shelf has been measured by Bender and Gow (1961) at Little America V (latitude 78°11'S, longitude 162°10'W) near the seaward edge of the shelf. The ice is about 260 m thick at this point and the measurements, which are shown in Figure 10.5, extended right through the shelf. It has so far proved difficult to fit any theoretical curve, derived under simple yet plausible assumptions, to these data.

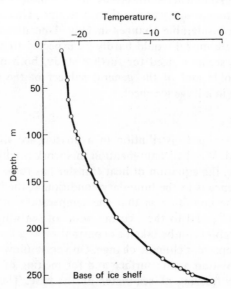

Fig. 10.5. Variation of temperature with depth in Ross Ice Shelf, Antarctica. From Bender and Gow (1961).

CHAPTER 11

THE RESPONSE OF A GLACIER TO CHANGES IN MASS BALANCE

"If God had consulted me before embarking on the Creation, I would have suggested something simpler."

ALFONSO OF CASTILE (15th century).

Introduction

The world's climate is continually changing, with apparently random fluctuations from year to year superimposed on long period trends: such changes are reflected in variations in the extent of glaciers. The repeated growth and decay of continental ice sheets during the Pleistocene is one example. The behaviour of glaciers in the European Alps during the 19th century provides another. Many of these glaciers reached maximum positions about 1820. They remained relatively far advanced for the next 40 or 50 years; minor retreats alternated with minor readvances. Most glaciers retreated rapidly between about 1865 and 1880, and then began a readvance which culminated shortly before 1900.

While advances and retreats of different glaciers appear to be broadly synchronous, the picture becomes more confused on closer examination of the records. Some glaciers in an area may be advancing while others are retreating. This is the case at present in the northwestern U.S.A. Some variations can be explained by differences between the local climates of individual glaciers. On the other hand, glaciers differ one from another in such features as size, steepness, and velocity. Hence different glaciers might be expected to react differently, or at least with different speeds, to a change in climate.

These ideas have been made more precise by theoretical analyses of how a glacier responds to a change in climate or, more accurately, in mass balance. Recent study of this subject began when Weertman (1958) and Nye (1958) rediscovered effects pointed out some fifty years earlier by de Marchi and Finsterwalder. Nye (1960, 1961, 1963a, 1963b, 1965b, 1965c) has greatly developed the theory; this chapter is an outline of his work.

A change in mass balance is not the only way in which climatic variations can affect glaciers. A long-term climatic change could alter the ice temperature and so change the rate of flow. Temperature changes are ignored in the theory which strictly applies only to temperate glaciers. Again, changes in weather might influence the glacier's velocity by varying the amount of water at the glacier bed. Omission of this factor from the theory is probably unimportant: fluctuations in the amount of water at the glacier bed are known to produce seasonal velocity variations, but there is no evidence that they cause long-term changes except perhaps during glacier surges. The present theory does not apply to surges in any case.

Basic Theory

Let x denote distance along the glacier measured from its head, and t denote time. Let Q be the *flow* or *discharge*, that is, the volume of ice passing, in unit time, through the cross-section at x. Let S be the cross-sectional area measured perpendicular to the x-axis, and W the width at the surface. Let b be the net mass balance averaged across the glacier at x. It is convenient here to measure b as ice thickness perpendicular to the surface rather than vertically. The quantities Q, S, W, and b are functions of x and t. The density of the glacier is assumed to be the same everywhere.

The condition that there is no change in mass of an element of ice is

$$\partial Q/\partial x + \partial S/\partial t = bW \qquad (1)$$

We now introduce the idea of a steady state. The net mass balance b varies continuously along the glacier; it is positive in the accumulation area and negative in the ablation area. If the value of b at each point remained constant for a long time, the glacier would eventually reach a steady state which we call the *datum state*. The x-axis is taken along the surface of this datum glacier which runs from $x = 0$ to $x = 1$. The quantities in equation (1) may be expressed as perturbations (suffix 1) from their values in the datum state (suffix 0). Thus

$$Q = Q_0 + Q_1 \qquad S = S_0 + S_1 \qquad bW = b_0 W_0 + (bW)_1$$

In the datum state, the cross-section does not change with time, so

$$\partial Q_0 / \partial x = b_0 W_0$$

Substitution of these values in (1) gives

$$\partial Q_1 / \partial x + \partial S_1 / \partial t = (bW)_1 \qquad (2)$$

For a valley glacier we can neglect the small perturbation in width. Therefore $W_1 = 0$. In addition, we can replace S_1 by $W_0 h_1$ where h denotes ice thickness. Equation (2) then becomes

$$\partial Q_1 / \partial x + W_0 \, \partial h_1 / \partial t = W_0 b_1 \qquad (3)$$

We must now make some assumption about the mechanism of flow. The discharge Q depends only on glacier width, ice thickness and velocity. The velocity u depends on ice thickness and surface slope α, namely

$$u = A_1 h^{n+1} \sin{}^n \alpha + A_2 h^m \sin{}^m \alpha \qquad (4)$$

where A_1, A_2, m, n are constants. The first term represents differential movement within the ice: the second, slip of the glacier on its bed (see Chapters 6 and 7). We therefore suppose that, at given x, Q is a function of h and α only. This assumption is fundamental to the theory. Although perhaps not strictly true in a real glacier, it should be a good approximation. The approximation could be improved, at the expense of complicating the mathematics, by making Q depend also on higher derivatives $\partial^2 h / \partial x^2$, $\partial^3 h / \partial^3 x$, ... ($\alpha$ equals the first derivative $-\partial h / \partial x$, if the slope of the glacier bed is constant). The dependence of Q on x includes

implicitly its dependence on other variables, such as roughness and slope of the bed and shape of the valley's cross-section,
which depend only on x. (Note the two alternative ways of regard-
ing Q. Initially Q was taken to be a function of x and t. Now we
are considering Q as a function of x, h, and α.)

From now on we suppose that perturbations from the datum
state are small. We can then, at any given x, expand Q_1 in terms
of h_1 and α_1 and neglect terms of second and higher orders.
Thus

$$Q_1 = c_0 h_1 + D_0 \alpha_1$$

where $c_0 = (\partial Q/\partial h)_0$ and $D_0 = (\partial Q/\partial \alpha)_0$. Now $\partial h/\partial x = \beta - \alpha$ where
β is the slope of the glacier bed. Since, for given x, β does not
change with time, $\partial h_1/\partial x = -\alpha_1$. The expansion can then be
written

$$Q_1 = c_0 h_1 - D_0(\partial h_1/\partial x) \tag{5}$$

Equations (3) and (5) are the fundamental equations of the
theory. They are two simultaneous partial differential equations
for determining the increase in discharge $Q_1 (x, t)$ and increase
in thickness $h_1 (x, t)$ which result from a given increase $b_1 (x, t)$
in mass balance. Here $c_0 (x)$, $D_0 (x)$, $W_0 (x)$ are regarded as
known functions of x: they specify the glacier completely.

Kinematic Waves

First we shall simplify the problem by taking a glacier of infinite width and by disregarding the dependence of Q on α.
Equation (1) can then be written

$$\partial q/\partial x + \partial h/\partial t = b \tag{1'}$$

Here q is the discharge per unit width. Also, since q does not
depend on α,

$$\partial q/\partial t = (\partial q/\partial h)_x (\partial h/\partial t) = c(\partial h/\partial t) \text{ say.} \tag{6}$$

But $q = uh$. (In this theory we do not distinguish between the
surface velocity and the velocity averaged over the ice thickness.)

Thus

$$c = u + h(\partial u/\partial h)$$

and so, by (4)

$$c = (n+2)u_d + (m+1)u_b \qquad (7)$$

where u_d, u_b are the velocities due to differential movement in the ice, and to sliding. As n is about 3 or 4 and m about 2, c ranges from about 3 to 6 times u according to the relative sizes of u_d and u_b. We shall take 4 as an average figure. From (1') and (6)

$$c(\partial q/\partial x) + \partial q/\partial t = cb \qquad (8)$$

If $b = 0$, equation (8) represents a "wave", on which q is constant, travelling down the glacier with velocity c. (If c were constant, $q = A \cos(x - ct)$ would be a solution.) This is an example of a *kinematic wave*, a type of motion studied by Lighthill and Whitham (1955). Their theory had already been applied to problems of flood waves on rivers and traffic flow on roads, before Nye applied it to glaciers. Kinematic waves are of fundamental importance: they are the means by which the effects of mass balance changes are propagated down the glacier. In the present sense, the word "wave" does not imply a travelling wave train, but merely a point moving with velocity c, different from the ice velocity, and carrying with it a particular property. In this case the property is that q remains constant. When b is not zero, the property of the wave is that, at a point moving with velocity c, q changes at rate b per unit distance. As ice velocity is a function of distance x, so is c. In glaciers, the wave velocity is greater than the ice velocity because velocity increases with ice thickness. In traffic flow, however, an increase in the concentration of vehicles decreases their velocity, and so the wave velocity is less than the vehicle velocity.

Kinematic waves should not be confused with dynamic waves, such as ocean waves. The existence of kinematic waves is a consequence of a conservation law (conservation of mass or vehicles for example), whenever there is a relation between discharge (mass passing a point in unit time), concentration (mass per unit distance), and position. Dynamic waves depend on Newton's Second Law combined with some relation between stress or force and displacement, strain, or curvature. Dynamic waves do not occur in glaciers because ice velocities are so low that the inertia term in the equation of motion is negligible compared with the gravity and "viscous" terms. Because the kinematic wave equation is of first order, the wave velocity has only one value. Thus kinematic waves are propagated in the downstream direction only.

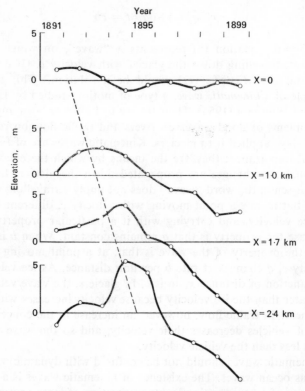

FIG. 11.1. Changes of mean surface elevation of Mer de Glace, France, along four cross-profiles over a period of 9 years. The broken line corresponds to a wave velocity of 800 m y^{-1}. From Lliboutry (1958a).

Have kinematic waves been observed in real glaciers? Any glacier is continually adjusting to a complex series of seasonal and long-term fluctuations in its mass balance. Diffusion of kinematic waves also increases the difficulty of distinguishing them. Thus it is not easy to observe a single wave moving down a glacier. However, there are several records of waves, observed as bulges of increased thickness, travelling faster than the ice itself. Figure 11.1 is taken from a paper by Lliboutry (1958a). It shows mean surface elevations of the Mer de Glace, France, along four cross-profiles for each year from 1891 to 1899. A bulge of increased thickness was passing down the glacier at a speed of about 800 m y $^{-1}$. The ice velocity was about 150 m y $^{-1}$. In recent years, waves have been observed on the Mer de Glace and the nearby Glacier des Bossons by Finsterwalder (1959) and on Nisqually Glacier, U.S.A., by Meier and Johnson (1962).

Result of Increase in Mass Balance

If a glacier is in a steady state and the mass balance is suddenly increased by an amount B, assumed the same at all points, what is the change $h_1(x)$ in surface elevation at different times thereafter? As in the preceding section, we neglect the dependence of q on surface slope and we consider a glacier of infinite width. from (1′) the following equation for the perturbations can be obtained in the same way as (3) was derived from (1).

$$\partial q_1/\partial x + \partial h_1/\partial t = B \qquad (3')$$

Also, (5) reduces to

$$q_1 = c_0 h_1. \qquad (5')$$

Elimination of q_1 gives

$$\partial h_1/\partial t = B - c_0' h_1 - c_0 \, \partial h_1/\partial x \qquad (9)$$

where $c_0' = dc_0/dx$. As c_0 is about four times the ice velocity, c_0' is about four times the longitudinal strain rate. Equation (9) has to be solved for h_1 with B given, and with c_0, c_0' known for the particular glacier.

We shall consider a simple model glacier which extends from $x = 0$ to $x = 1$ with the equilibrium line at $x = \frac{1}{2}$. The longitudinal strain rate in a glacier is usually positive in the accumulation area and negative in the ablation area (see Chapter 6). So we take

$$c_0 = rx \qquad \text{when } x \leqslant \tfrac{1}{2} \qquad (10)$$

and

$$c_0 = r(1-x) \qquad \text{when } x \geqslant \tfrac{1}{2}$$

with r a positive constant.

Let us first try to find a solution in which h_1 does not change with x. Equation (9) then becomes

$$\partial h_1/\partial t = B - c_0' h_1$$

If $h_1 = 0$ at $t = 0$, the solution is

$$h_1 = Br^{-1}\,[1 - \exp\,(-rt)] \qquad \text{for } x < \tfrac{1}{2} \qquad (11)$$
$$h_1 = Br^{-1}\,[\exp\,(rt) - 1] \qquad \text{for } x > \tfrac{1}{2} \qquad (12)$$

Equation (11) shows that, where the longitudinal strain rate is positive, the glacier begins to thicken at rate B. The rate of thickening decreases exponentially with time and the glacier ultimately reaches a new steady state. The final change in thickness is B/r. Equation (12), on the other hand, shows that the response of a region of longitudinal compression is unstable. The initial rate of thickening is B, but the thickness continues to increase exponentially. Between the two regions there will be an area where the assumption, that $\partial h_1/\partial x$ is zero, breaks down. There will be a step in the surface because the region down glacier has thickened more than the region up glacier. This step is the start of a kinematic wave which moves down the glacier and, as we shall show, ultimately restores stability. On a real glacier any such step will be rounded by diffusion.

We can obtain the final values of h_1 if we assume that $\partial h_1/\partial t$ tends to zero as t tends to infinity. We therefore solve (9) with

$\partial h_1/\partial t = 0$, $\partial h_1/\partial x \doteqdot 0$, and c_0, c_0' given by (10). The solutions are easily verified to be

$$h_1 = B/r \qquad \text{for } x \leqslant \tfrac{1}{2} \qquad (13a)$$
$$h_1 = Bx/r(1-x) \qquad \text{for } x \geqslant \tfrac{1}{2} \qquad (13b)$$

The first solution is the same as that obtained by letting $t \to \infty$ in (11). The second solution is the value of h_1 that is reached after stability has been restored. We must terminate the solution a short distance before the terminus $x = 1$, because h_1 becomes infinite there. The solution does, however, show that, near the terminus, the response to a change in mass balance is very large.

These results can be obtained rigorously by solving the partial differential equation without taking either $\partial h_1/\partial x$ or $\partial h_1/\partial t$ to be zero. It is simpler to work with q_1 than h_1. If we eliminate h_1 between (3') and (5') we obtain

$$\partial q_1/\partial x + c_0^{-1}\,\partial q_1/\partial t = B \qquad (14)$$

with c_0 given by (10) as before, and B constant.

The standard method of solving this linear partial differential equation is to solve the simultaneous ordinary differential equations

$$dx = c_0 dt = B^{-1}\,dq_1 \qquad (15)$$

The first two expressions give

$$t = \int_{x_0}^{x} c_0^{-1}\,dx \qquad (16)$$

where $x = x_0$ at $t = 0$. This defines a set of curves called the characteristics. These represent the paths of the kinematic waves in the (x, t) plane. They are shown in Fig. 11.2. The part of the diagram for which $x > \tfrac{1}{2}$ is sub-divided into two regions according as the paths start on the axis $t = 0$ ("Region III") or cross

14*

the line $x = \frac{1}{2}$ ("Region II"). In Region II, (16) gives

$$t = \int_{x_0}^{1/2} \frac{dx}{rx} + \int_{1/2}^{x} \frac{dx}{r(1-x)}$$

$$4 x_0(1-x) = \exp(-rt)$$

Also, integration of (15) with $q_1 = 0$ at $t = 0$ that is, at $x = x_0$, gives

$$q_1 = B(x - x_0)$$

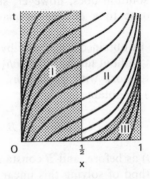

FIG. 11.2. Wave paths in the x,t plane for an idealized glacier. From Nye (1960).

Elimination of x_0 from the last two equations gives q_1, and since $h_1 = q_1/c_0$ by (5')

$$h_1 = Br^{-1} [x/(1-x) - \exp(-rt)/4(1-x)^2] \qquad (17)$$

This is the solution for Region II. It is a stable solution, which tends to (13b) as $t \to \infty$. This shows that the kinematic waves restore stability to the region $x > \frac{1}{2}$. Region III is the region which the kinematic wave from $x = \frac{1}{2}$ has not yet reached. The solution for this region is found to be the unstable solution (12). The stable solution (11) is found for $x < \frac{1}{2}$.

These solutions are plotted in Fig. 11.3 which shows the increase in thickness of the model glacier at different times after a sudden increase in mass balance. In the accumulation area, the surface rises towards its new steady state value at an exponentially decreasing rate. In the ablation area, the surface initially rises and at an increasing rate. The rate of rise starts to decrease at any given point when the kinematic wave from the point

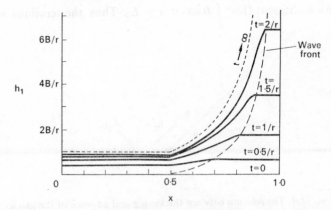

FIG. 11.3. The increase h_1 in thickness in an idealized glacier at various times t after a sudden uniform increase B in mass balance. The upper part responds stably; the lower part responds unstably until the kinematic wave from $x = \frac{1}{2}$ arrives. From Nye (1960).

$x = \frac{1}{2}$ arrives. (The broken line shows the path of this wave.) The line marked $t \to \infty$ shows the final increase in thickness. This increase is very large near the terminus and so the glacier will make a considerable advance. These are the results of a sudden increase in mass balance, that is, an increase in accumulation in the accumulation area and a decrease in ablation in the ablation area. A sudden decrease in mass balance makes the whole glacier thinner. The effect is large near the terminus: a small reduction in mass balance causes a substantial retreat.

The amount of advance or retreat can be found by a simple geometrical argument (see Fig. 11.4). The length of the glacier in its datum state, L_0, is given by

$$\int_0^{L_0} b_0 \, \mathrm{d}x = 0$$

At the terminus of the glacier q_0 is zero. However, when the mass balance has maintained the value $b_0 + B$ for a long time, there will be an additional flow $\int_0^{L_0} B \, \mathrm{d}x$ at $x = L_0$. Thus the terminus will

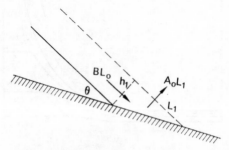

Fig. 11.4. The relation between thickening and advance of the glacier terminus. From Nye (1960).

have advanced for some distance L_1, measured parallel to the surface. Moreover, if A_0 is the ablation rate at the terminus, and B is small,

$$\int_0^{L_0} B \, \mathrm{d}x = A_0 L_1$$

Thus, if B is constant,

$$L_1/L_0 = B/A_0$$

For example, if A_0 is 5 m y^{-1} and the mass balance increases uniformly by 0·5 m y^{-1}, the length of the glacier will ultimately increase by 10 per cent.

This argument has shown that the total distance a glacier will advance or retreat, for a given change in mass balance, does not depend on kinematic wave phenomena. The total distance is determined solely by conservation of volume.

Observations confirm this instability of glacier termini: lateral moraines and trimlines are often close to the present surface of a glacier in its upper reaches, but far above it near the terminus. This large response to small mass balance changes means that glaciers are sensitive indicators of climatic changes. The problem, as we shall see, is to interpret the indications in detail.

Instability of Region of Compressing Flow

The instability of a region of compressing flow can also be demonstrated in the following way.

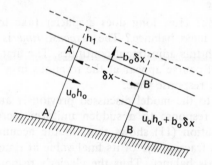

Fig. 11.5. Instability of region of compressing flow. From Nye (1960).

Figure 11.5 shows a small length δx of the glacier in its ablation area. In a steady state, flow through the upper surface must just balance ablation. This flow must also equal the difference between the discharges through AA' and BB'. If the discharge through AA' is $u_0 h_0$, that through BB' is therefore $u_0 h_0 + b_0 \delta x$, where b_0 is negative.

Now suppose that a layer of thickness h_1 is suddenly laid on the glacier surface. The velocity will increase to $u_0 + u_1$. The discharge will increase by $u_0 h_1$ because of the increase in thickness and by $u_1 h_0$ because of the increase in velocity. But u is proportional to h^m and so $u_1/u_0 = m h_1/h_0$. It follows that the discharge through AA' has increased by $(m+1)\,u_0 h_1$. This shows that the increase in discharge through a section is proportional to the steady state velocity there.

Flow is assumed to be compressing and so the steady state velocity at BB' is less than at AA'. Thus the increase in discharge through BB', as a result of adding the layer h_1 to the surface, is less than the increase in discharge through AA'. Ice therefore accumulates between the two sections and the surface level must rise further. This shows that the region is unstable.

This argument shows that the instability of a region of compressing flow is merely a consequence of conservation of volume: it has nothing to do with kinematic waves.

Response Time

We now ask: How long does a glacier take to adjust to a change in its mass balance? The *response time* is the order of time for which this adjustment continues. The first effects of the change will of course appear at the terminus in a much shorter time than the response time.

We return to the model discussed previously and, as before, consider the response to a sudden uniform increase in mass balance. Equation (11) shows that, in the accumulation area, h_1 is within a fraction $1/e$ of its final value at time $1/r$ after the change in mass balance. Thus the glacier's response time is of order $1/r$. Figure 11.3 shows that, by this time, the kinematic wave from $x = \frac{1}{2}$ has reached $x = 0.8$ approximately and the thickness change there has reached about half its final value. Now r is about four times the longitudinal strain rate. Typical values of strain rate in valley glaciers are between 10^{-1} and $10^{-2}\,\mathrm{y}^{-1}$, so their response times should be in the range 2.5 to 25 years. The greater the strain rate, the quicker the glacier can adjust to changing conditions. We shall see later, however, that diffusion of the kinematic waves lengthens these times appreciably.

We can also calculate the response time of a large ice sheet. Longitudinal strain rates in the accumulation areas of the Greenland and Antarctic ice sheets appear to be of the order of

10^{-4} y^{-1}. The corresponding response time is 2500 years. Equation (11) shows that an increase of B in mass balance will ultimately produce an increase B/r in thickness. For example, with $B = 1·5$ cm y^{-1}, which would be a 10 per cent increase in precipitation in Antarctica, the final h_1 is 37·5 m. This is only 1 or 2 per cent of the ice thickness. This confirms a result derived in Chapter 9: the thickness of an ice sheet is insensitive to changes in accumulation.

Diffusion of Kinematic Waves

In the preceding theory we took account of the dependence of velocity, and hence of discharge, on ice thickness, but ignored its dependence on surface slope. This may be a reasonable simpli-

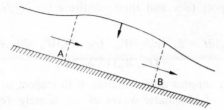

FIG. 11.6. Diffusion of kinematic wave.

fication for some glaciers, but in general it cannot be justified. When discharge Q is a function of surface slope α, kinematic waves undergo diffusion, as the following simple argument shows.

In Fig. 11.6, ice thicknesses at A and B are equal, but there is a bulge (a kinematic wave) between the two points. Thus the slope at B is greater than at A. Since $\partial Q/\partial \alpha$ is positive, because $\partial u/\partial \alpha$ is, Q at B is greater than Q at A. The surface elevation between A and B will therefore decrease. The bulge of high h and high Q between A and B is thus diminished, and this is what is meant by diffusion of a kinematic wave.

The basic equations are

$$\partial Q_1/\partial x + W_0(\partial h_1/\partial t) = W_0 b_1 \tag{3}$$

$$Q_1 = c_0 h_1 - D_0(\partial h_1/\partial x) \tag{5}$$

Here $c_0(x) = (\partial Q/\partial h)_0$, $D_0(x) = (\partial Q/\partial \alpha)_0$, and W_0 is the width of the glacier in the datum state. For simplicity, take W_0 as constant and b_1 as a function of t but not x. Differentiation of (3) with respect to x and (5) with respect to t, followed by elimination of h_1, gives the equation for Q_1:

$$\partial Q_1/\partial t = c_0 b_1 - (c_0/W_0)\,(\partial Q_1/\partial x) + (D_0/W_0)\,(\partial^2 Q_1/\partial x^2) \quad (18)$$

This is a diffusion equation in which c_0/W_0 is the velocity of propagation of perturbations of discharge Q_1, that is, the kinematic wave velocity, and D_0/W_0 is the diffusion coefficient for kinematic waves. In previous sections we treated the special case $D_0 = 0$.

To obtain an equation for h_1 instead of Q_1, we differentiate (5) with respect to x and then substitute for $\partial Q_1/\partial x$ in (3). The result is

$$\partial h_1/\partial t = b_1 - c_0' h_1/W_0 - (c_0 - D_0')W_0^{-1}(\partial h_1/\partial x) +$$
$$(D_0/W_0)\,(\partial^2 h_1/\partial x^2) \quad (19)$$

Here a dash denotes differentiation with respect to x. Note that the velocity of kinematic waves of h_1, namely $(c_0 - D_0')/W_0$ is now different from the velocity c_0/W_0 of kinematic waves of Q_1. With no diffusion, the two velocities are equal. As before, c_0 is about four times the ice velocity. Equation (4) shows that ice velocity, and therefore Q, is proportional to $\sin^m \alpha$ where m is about 3, and so

$$D_0 = (\partial Q/\partial \alpha)_0 = 3Q_0 \cot \alpha_0 \quad (20)$$

The values of c_0 and D_0 at the glacier terminus need further examination. Field observations show that the ice velocity at the terminus is not usually zero, even though the ice thickness is. Thus, near the terminus, we must take u independent of h and so the discharge will be proportional to h not h^4. It follows that, near the terminus $c_0 = u_0$, not $4u_0$. We can assume that there is a gradual transition between these two values as the terminus is approached. There is no need to modify the relation between Q and α, so (20) remains true at the terminus. We can regard θ_0, the angle of the wedge-shaped terminus, as given by observation.

Thus a change in thickness h_1 at the datum position of the terminus can be related to an advance L_1, measured parallel to the glacier bed, by the equation

$$L_1 = h_1 \operatorname{cosec} \theta_0 \tag{21}$$

We now adopt the same approach as before. We consider a model glacier in which c_0 and D_0 are simple functions of x and, by solving equation (18) or (19), find the perturbation in discharge Q_1 or in thickness h_1 produced by a change b_1 in mass balance. The functions chosen for c_0 and D_0 should be such that an exact solution of equation (18) is possible and the values of c_0 and D_0 should be values which might be found for a real glacier. The functions are

$$c_0 = (x/\sigma)(1-x/L) \tag{22}$$

$$D_0 = (Ex^2/\sigma)(1-\delta-x/L) \tag{23}$$

The datum glacier extends from $x = 0$ to $L(1-\delta)$, with the equilibrium line at $x = L/2$. Here σ, E, δ are constants; σ has the dimensions of time, E and δ are dimensionless, and δ is small. In this model, c_0 and D_0 are zero at the head of the glacier and D_0 is zero at the terminus. By taking the terminus at $L(1-\delta)$ rather than at L, we have made c_0 non-zero there. The longitudinal strain rate is positive above the equilibrium line and negative below it. In addition, there is no discontinuity in c_0'. (There was in the previous model.)

We shall now estimate typical values for the constants. Taking $x = L/2$ in (22) gives

$$\sigma = L/4\,c_0 = L/16\,u_0$$

where c_0 and u_0 are maximum values since they refer to the equilibrium line. If $L = 10$ km and $u_0 = 100$ m y^{-1}, $\sigma = 6$ years. Taking $x = L/2$ in (23) gives

$$D_0 = EL^2/8\sigma$$

since δ is small. But by (20)

$$D_0 = 3u_0h_0 \cot \alpha_0$$

Thus

$$E = (24 \, \sigma u_0 h_0 \cot \alpha_0)/L^2 = (3h_0 \cot \alpha_0)/2L$$

where u_0, h_0, α_0 denote values at $x = L/2$. If $L = 10$ km, $h_0 = 250$ m, $\alpha_0 = 3°$, then $E = 0.75$.

Taking $x = L(1-\delta)$ in (22) gives

$$c_0 = L\delta/\sigma \qquad (24)$$

because δ^2 can be neglected. But, at the terminus, $c_0 = u_0 = 10$ m y^{-1} say. With the previous values of L and σ, this gives $\delta = 0.006$.

Thus, very roughly, $\sigma = 5$ years, $E = 0.5$ to 1.0, $\delta = 0.005$. Values will vary appreciably, however, from glacier to glacier. Different values of E correspond to different amounts of diffusion.

To simplify the mathematics, take L as unit of length and σ as unit of time. Equations (22) and (23) become

$$c_0 = x(1-x) \qquad (22')$$
$$D_0 = Ex^2(1-\delta-x) \qquad (23')$$

How Diffusion Affects the Response

We now consider the response of the model glacier to a sudden increase B in mass balance, assumed the same for all x. First we determine the steady state values, which will hold after the glacier has adjusted to the new conditions, by putting $\partial h_1/\partial t = 0$. In this case it is simpler to use equations (3) and (5) rather than (18), which was derived from them. Equation (3), for unit glacier width, becomes

$$\partial q_1/\partial x = B$$

Thus

$$q_1 = Bx$$

because $q_1 = 0$ at $x = 0$.

Equation (5) then becomes

$$Bx = x(1-x)h_1 - Ex^2(1-\delta-x)(\partial h_1/\partial x)$$

For $E = 1$, the solution is

$$h_1 = B(1 + x/\delta) \qquad (25)$$

as is easily verified.

For no diffusion, $E = 0$, and

$$h_1 = B/(1 - x) \qquad (26)$$

These, along with solutions obtained by Nye (1963a) for other values of E, are shown in Fig. 11.7.

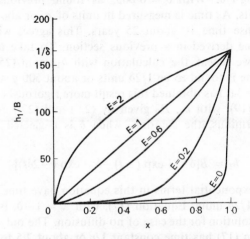

FIG. 11.7. Steady-state profiles of idealized glacier after a sudden uniform increase B in net mass balance, for different amounts of diffusion. From Nye (1963a).

The two important conclusions are:

1. The terminus ultimately thickens by the same amount, B/δ, whatever the amount of diffusion (including no diffusion). The final advance will therefore be the same in all cases.

2. Except near the terminus, the final thickening is much greater with diffusion than it is without.

From the last statement, we might expect diffusion to increase the glacier's response time. The following rough calculation confirms this. If V_1 is the volume of ice which must be added to unit width of the glacier to attain the new profile,

$$V_1 = \int_0^{1-\delta} h_1 \, dx$$

For no diffusion, h_1 is given by (26) and $V_1 = B \log 1/\delta$. But the volume added to unit width of the glacier in unit time is $B(1-\delta)$. Thus the time to reach the steady state profile is approximately $\log 1/\delta$. With $\delta = 0.005$, as found previously, this is 5 time units. As time is measured in units of σ, or about 5 years, the response time is about 25 years. This agrees with the response time derived in a previous section. To take account of diffusion we repeat the calculation with h_1 as in (25). The response time is found to be $1/2\delta$ units or about 500 years.

Nye (1963a) has obtained this result more rigorously by solving equation (19), with c_0, D_0 given by (22') and (23') and $E = 1$. At the terminus, the solution, when δ is neglected compared with 1, is

$$h_1 = B[\delta^{-1} + \exp(-t) - \delta^{-1} \exp(-2\delta t)] \qquad (27)$$

The two exponential terms in this equation have time constants of 1 and $1/2\delta$ units. Equation (17), with $x = 1-\delta$, is a corresponding solution for the case of no diffusion. The only exponential term in (17) has time constant $1/r$ or about 2.5 to 25 years.

Differentiation of (27) gives

$$\partial h_1/\partial t = B[2 \exp(-2\delta t) - \exp(-t)]$$

Since $\delta \ll 1$, $\exp(-2\delta t) \gg \exp(-t)$, except near $t = 0$. Thus the equation shows that $\partial h_1/\partial t$ is initially equal to B, then increases rapidly to nearly $2B$, and then decreases to zero exponentially with time constant $1/2\delta$. The period when $\partial h_1/\partial t$ is increasing is the unstable period discussed previously, but these values of $\partial h_1/\partial t$ are much smaller than the values in the previous case. Thus diffusion both slows down the rate of adjustment and increases the amount of adjustment needed. The response time is therefore increased appreciably.

Equation (24) shows that the numerical value of the long time constant ($1/2\delta$ units or $\sigma/2\delta$ years) is obtained by dividing the length of the glacier by twice the velocity at the terminus. This ratio will vary widely from one glacier to another, but it will probably be measured in hundreds rather than tens of years. The previous numerical estimates suggested that the value $E = 1$, chosen so that the equations would have an exact solution, may be a relatively high value for a real glacier. Figure 11.7 shows that decreasing the amount of diffusion reduces the total change in the glacier profile. In this case the response time will also be reduced.

The Frequency Response of a Glacier

Changes in mass balance can be represented more realistically by harmonic functions than by the step function used in the previous discussions. In this case, equation (19) has to be solved with $b_1 = B \exp(i\omega t)$, where B is a constant, c_0 and D_0 are given by (22') and (23') with $E = 1$, and $W_0 = 1$. The solution is a special case of the general solution given in the next section, so we shall merely state that it is

$$h_1(x, t) = H(x, \omega) \exp(i\omega t)$$

Thus h_1 varies harmonically with the same angular frequency ω as b_1, but with different phase. (The solution must be of this form because the differential equations are linear.) The solution at the terminus is shown in Fig. 11.8 as graphs of (a) amplitude $|H|/B$, (b) phase lag φ of maxima of h_1 behind maxima of b_1, (c) time lag φ/ω, versus ω. These curves may be called the *frequency response* of the glacier, by analogy with an electrical circuit.

Curve (a) shows that only for very long period changes (of the order of 10,000 years) does the terminus reach the maximum thickness B/δ which it would attain in response to a step function. Curve (b) shows that the phase lag tends to zero for very long period changes (10,000 years) and to 90° for very short period changes (1 year or less). This is what one might expect. The glacier should be able to keep in adjustment with very slow changes in mass balance. On the other hand, there will not be time for ice flow to play any part in the response to very rapid changes. In this case, equation (3′) becomes $\partial h_1/\partial t = b_1$. This shows that maxima and minima of h_1 occur when b_1 is zero; in other words the phase lag is 90°. Seasonal variations are short period changes; a 90° phase lag means that h_1 is maximum at the end of the winter and minimum at the end of the summer, as observed.

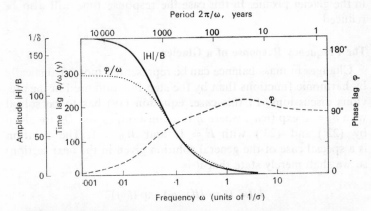

FIG. 11.8. Response at the terminus of an idealized glacier to an oscillation in net mass balance of amplitude B and frequency ω. The curves show the amplitude of the thickness change, and the phase lag and the time lag between a mass balance maximum and a thickness maximum, as functions of ω. The scales of period and time lag correspond to a value of 6 years for the time unit σ. From Nye (1965c).

Curve (c) in Fig. 11.8 shows how the time lag φ/ω varies with the period of the mass balance change. The time lag is roughly one quarter of the period, provided the period is less than about 600 years. For example, the time lag for a change with period 40 years is about 10 years. In such a change, the glacier will start to advance 10 years after the mass balance is at a minimum; the terminus will be furthest forward 10 years after the maximum mass balance. If the mass balance returns to its datum value and stays there, the glacier will take a few hundred years (the response time) to reach its datum state. This example should make clear the distinction between time lag and response time. The time lag is the interval between maximum (and minimum) mass balance and maximum (and minimum) terminal position. The response time is the period during which adjustment to a given mass balance change continues.

General Solution

The solution when the perturbation of mass balance is an arbitrary function of time can be derived from the result for a step function. The method, which has been used by Lliboutry (1965, p. 751), is similar to one used to calculate the response of an electrical circuit to an applied voltage.

The right-hand side of (27) with $B = 1$, represents the response of the glacier terminus, at time t, to a unit step function increase of mass balance at time zero. Denote it by $H(t)$. Because the differential equations are linear, the response at time t to a step function db_1 at time zero will be $db_1 H(t)$, and to one at time τ will be $db_1 H(t-\tau)$. An arbitrary function $b_1(t)$ can be approximated by a "staircase function" that is, the sum of a large number of small step functions of amplitude db_1 at successive times. The sum starts at time $\tau = -\infty$, when b_1 is assumed to be zero, and ends at time $\tau = t$. Thus the response to $b_1(t)$ is

$$h_1(t) = \int_{-\infty}^{t} \frac{db_1}{d\tau} H(t-\tau) \, d\tau \qquad (28)$$

(Readers wishing a detailed derivation of this result should consult a book on electrical network theory, such as Seshu and Balabanian (1959, pp. 206–7).)

Integration of (28) by parts gives

$$h_1(t) = [b_1(\tau) H(t-\tau)]_{-\infty}^{t} + \int_{-\infty}^{t} b_1(\tau) \dot{H}(t-\tau) \, d\tau$$

where $\dot{H}$ denotes dH/dt. The first term on the right-hand side is zero because $b_1 = 0$ at $t = -\infty$, and $H(0) = 0$ by the initial condition that $h_1 = 0$ at $t = 0$. Substitution for H of the value obtained by differentiating (27) with respect to t with $B = 1$, gives

$$h_1(t) = -\bar{b}_1 + \delta^{-1}\bar{\bar{b}}_1 \qquad (29)$$

where

$$\bar{b}_1 = \int_{-\infty}^{t} b_1(\tau) \exp\left[-(t-\tau)\right] d\tau$$

$$\bar{\bar{b}}_1 = 2\delta \int_{-\infty}^{t} b_1(\tau) \exp\left[-2\delta(t-\tau)\right] d\tau$$

Equation (29) is the change in thickness at the terminus produced by a mass balance change which is an arbitrary function of time but has the same value for all x. The quantities $\bar{b}_1$ and $\bar{\bar{b}}_1$ are averages of b_1 over past time. The term in the integral for $\bar{b}_1$ is only appreciable over a time interval of order one unit. However, in the integral for $\bar{\bar{b}}_1$, one has to take values of b_1 over an interval of order $1/2\delta$ before the exponential factor makes the term negligibly small.

Inverse Problem

Let us now look at the inverse problem: Given the variations in thickness h_1 at the terminus of the datum glacier over a period of time, to find the variations in mass balance which produced them. Differentiation of (29) twice with respect to time gives, if δ is neglected compared with 1,

$$\dot{h}_1 = b_1 + \bar{b}_1 - 2\bar{\bar{b}}_1 \qquad (30)$$

$$\ddot{h}_1 = \dot{b}_1 + b_1 - \bar{b}_1 + 4\delta\bar{\bar{b}}_1 \qquad (31)$$

where we have used the relations

$$d\bar{b}_1/dt = b_1 - \bar{b}_1$$

$$d\bar{\bar{b}}_1/dt = 2\delta(b_1 - \bar{b}_1)$$

Elimination of $\bar{b}_1$, $\bar{\bar{b}}_1$ between (29), (30), (31) gives, since $\delta \ll 1$,

$$\dot{b}_1 + 2b_1 = \ddot{h}_1 + \dot{h}_1 + 2\delta h_1$$

This is a differential equation for b_1. The solution is given by

$$b_1 \exp(2t) = \int_{-\infty}^{t} (\ddot{h}_1 + \dot{h}_1 + 2\delta h_1) \exp(2\tau)\, d\tau$$

Integration of the right-hand side by parts gives

$$b_1 \exp(2t) = \dot{h}_1 \exp(2t) - h_1 \exp(2t) + 2(1+\delta) \int_{-\infty}^{t} h_1 \exp(2\tau)\, d\tau$$

or

$$b_1 = \dot{h}_1 - h_1 + \bar{h}_1 \tag{32}$$

where

$$\bar{h}_1 = 2 \int_{-\infty}^{t} h_1 \exp\left[-2(t-\tau)\right] d\tau$$

and we have replaced $1 + \delta$ by 1 since δ is small.

Equation (32) shows that, to determine the current value of b_1 from measurements of h_1 at the terminus, we need to know the current values of h_1 and $\dot{h}_1$, and also the average value of h_1 over past time. The time scale of this average is half a time unit, that is, a few years. (Time is measured in units of σ, or about 5 years.) No long-term average of h_1 occurs in (32).

There is thus a curious asymmetry between the two problems. To explain a glacier's current behaviour we need mass balance data extending over several hundred years. To calculate the current mass balance we need only a few years' record of terminus fluctuations. The difference seems reasonable. As h_1 represents an integration of b_1 over past time, a long record is needed. Conversely, b_1 must be a kind of time derivative of h_1, and to determine a derivative at t, only values in the neighbourhood of t are required.

We now turn from the analysis of special models to the calculation of the response of a real glacier.

Application to Particular Glaciers

The extent to which the detailed behaviour of a particular glacier can be calculated is limited by the amount of data available. Continuous records of terminal positions may go back 50 or 100 years: study of moraines may provide some information over a much longer period. On very few glaciers has the mass balance been measured continuously for 10 years: on none does the record cover more than 25 years. Thus we should be able to calculate mass balance from available data on terminal positions and, in a few cases, compare these with measured mass balances. But a calculation of the present behaviour of the terminus of any glacier is not possible because this, as we have seen, requires mass balance data extending over several hundred years. We can, however, calculate the frequency response.

In both types of problem, the differential equations have to be solved by a numerical method. The quantities $c_0(x)$ and $D_0(x)$ are now given numerically instead of as algebraic functions. Their values are calculated as follows.

We need to know the ice thickness and surface slope at points along the entire glacier. These quantities refer to a datum state, that is, the dimensions the glacier would have after its net mass balance had remained constant for a long time. There is an infinite number of possible datum states, but no real glacier is ever in any of them. We therefore select, from the possible states, one in which the surface is close to the present glacier surface. In a datum state

$$\int_0^L b_0 W_0 \, dx = 0 \tag{33}$$

Here L is length and b is net mass balance averaged across the glacier at the point x. For the width W_0 we use measured values. The terminus of the datum glacier must be wedge-shaped to fit the theoretical model. Therefore the length L is that of a glacier with a wedge-shaped terminus of area equal to the terminal area of the actual glacier. To determine b_0, we draw a graph of measured b against x (the mean of several years' observations) and displace it upwards or downwards until the integral in (33) is zero.

Next the datum discharge $Q_0(x)$ is calculated from

$$Q_0 = \int_0^x b_0 W_0 \, dx$$

and $D_0(x)$ from (20)

$$D_0 = 3Q_0 \cot \alpha_0$$

For α_0 we use the measured surface slope, averaged across the glacier at x. The average velocity $u_0(x)$ through a section, in the datum state, is then computed from

$$Q_0 = (\tfrac{2}{3}) u_0 W_0 h_0$$

where h_0 is the measured ice thickness on the centreline of the glacier. The factor $\tfrac{2}{3}$ appears because the cross-section is assumed to be a parabola. Finally, $c_0(x)$ is calculated from

$$c_0 = \begin{cases} 4W_0 u_0 & \text{not near } x = L \\ W_0 u_0 & \text{near } x = L \end{cases}$$

This change of multiplier was explained previously.

The frequency response of a given glacier is calculated from the basic equations (3) and (5), with $b_1 = \exp i\omega t$. Since the differential equations are linear, the final response will consist of variations of h_1 and Q_1 of the same frequency (ω) as b_1 but of different phase. We therefore write

$$h_1(x, t) = H(x, \omega) \exp i\omega t$$
$$Q_1(x, t) = Q(x, \omega) \exp i\omega t$$

where H and Q are, in general, complex. Substitution in (3) and (5) gives

$$Q' + i\omega W_0 H = W_0$$
$$Q = c_0 H - D_0 H'$$

where dashes denote derivatives with respect to x. Nye (1965c) has devised a numerical method of solving these equations using a computer.

Nye (1965b) has also devised a numerical method for the inverse problem. In this case we are given $L_1(t)$, the distance between the actual terminus and the datum terminus at times t, one year apart. Distances are converted into thicknesses h_1 by equation (21), using the angle θ_0 measured at the actual terminus. The problem is to find what function $b_1(t)$ in (19) will give the observed $h_1(L, t)$. Note that b_1 is assumed to be the same for all x. Because the system is linear and perturbations are supposed to be small, the column vectors $\mathbf{h}(n)$, $\mathbf{b}(n)$ of annual values of h_1 and b_1 can be assumed to be related in the form

$$\mathbf{h} = E\mathbf{b} \qquad (34)$$

Here E is a matrix in which all the rows are the same, but each successive row is moved one place to the right. All the elements below the leading diagonal are zero. Nye has called the matrix elements *influence coefficients*. Equation (28) is the analogue of (34) in the continuous case when the time interval between observations tends to zero. The values of the influence coefficients can be obtained by a process which is essentially a numerical integration of the diffusion equation. The terms in $\mathbf{b}$ are then found from the given $\mathbf{h}$ by inverting equation (34). A computer is needed.

Nye has made these calculations for South Cascade Glacier in northwest U.S.A. and Stor Glacier in Sweden. These are two of the very few glaciers for which there are enough data to apply these methods. Meier and Tangborn (1965) have determined the mass balance of South Cascade Glacier each year since 1952, and the terminus record goes back 35 years. Schytt (1962) and others have measured the mass balance and terminal position of Stor Glacier annually since 1945. Isolated observations extend the terminus record back to 1897. South Cascade Glacier has been retreating throughout the observation period; Stor Glacier since about 1920. Both glaciers are about 3 km^2 in area.

The computed frequency response curves suggest that diffusion was much less important on these glaciers than in the theoretical model with $E = 1$. A value of about 0·1 was more suitable. Time lags, for changes with periods of 100 years or less, are roughly $\frac{1}{4}$ of the period (90° phase lag). Even for very long period changes, however, the time lag never exceeds 42 years for South Cascade Glacier and 56 years for Stor Glacier, in contrast to a few hundred years for the model with $E = 1$. This shows that computations should be made for glaciers of various sizes and in various environments.

For each glacier, annual mass balances, calculated from changes in terminal position, were compared with measured values. There were considerable discrepancies between the two. Inaccuracies in measuring retreat can probably explain these. The theory includes the assumption that the terminus is wedge-shaped and that it moves back evenly at all points. In fact, the amount of retreat often varies along the terminus and it is normally measured at only one place. Also, the measurements should be made at the end of the ablation season; this was seldom done. A further complication for South Cascade Glacier is that part of its terminus calves into a lake. To reduce the effects of such inaccuracies, the data were smoothed by taking 10 year running means. Differences between observed and calculated values of these means were small.

Summary

The following are the basic assumptions.

1. The discharge Q is, to a good approximation, a function of distance x, ice thickness h, and surface slope α.

This relation is reasonably well established. The form of the function doesn't have to be specified. (It only has to be specified in numerical calculations for particular models.) The dependence of Q on x includes its dependence on all other variables which are functions of x but not of time. These facts make the theory very general.

This assumption will not hold unless two other conditions, among others, are met:

1a. The temperature of the glacier is uniform.

1b. The effects of changes in the amount of meltwater at the glacier bed are ignored.

Thus the theory strictly applies only to temperate glaciers. It should also apply to those changes in cold glaciers which result from changes in mass balance; but climate may also influence cold glaciers by changing the ice temperature. There is no evidence that changes in the amount of meltwater produce long-term changes in glaciers, expect perhaps during surges (see Chapter 8).

2. Volume is conserved. This is equivalent to conservation of mass because density is assumed to be constant.

3. Perturbations are small.

Thus the theory applies to "normal" slow advances and retreats, but not to surges.

4. The mass balance perturbation (b_1) is a function of time only.

To let b_1 depend on x as well would complicate the mathematics. Data from South Cascade Glacier support the assumption that b_1 is the same for all x; data from Stor Glacier do not (see Chapter 3). Perhaps b_1 might also depend on h_1 for, as the glacier thickens, the altitude of the surface rises, and this could result in increased accumulation and decreased ablation. Such an effect would lead to an instability, described for the case of an ice sheet in Chapter 9. This is a different type of instability from that discussed in the present chapter.

The following are the main conclusions. As a result of the functional form of Q and the law of mass conservation, variations in mass balance are propagated down the glacier as kinematic waves of increased and decreased flow. The wave velocity is about four times the ice velocity. The lower parts of the glacier, where flow is compressing, are temporarily unstable. They therefore start to thicken rapidly in response to an increase in mass balance. Stability is restored by the arrival of kinematic waves from higher up the glacier; but a small increase in mass balance may result in considerable thickening near the terminus, and thus in a substantial advance. Diffusion of kinematic waves is a result of the dependence of Q on surface slope. Except at the terminus, the difference between the new and old steady state profiles is much greater when diffusion is taken into account than when it is ignored. Diffusion also decreases the rate of change of thickness. The response time is therefore greatly increased: the adjustment of most glaciers to a change in mass balance may continue for several hundred years. For harmonic variations in mass balance with periods of a few hundred years or less, maxima and minima of terminal position lag behind maxima and minima of mass balance by roughly one quarter of the period.

These conclusions are derived from simple mathematical models. They help to explain several observed features of glacier behaviour. Because the response time is long, there are no data suitable for numerical prediction of the current behaviour of any glacier. However, the inverse problem, to calculate mass balance variations from measurements of advance or retreat, only requires data for periods of the order of 10 years. Data adequate even for this are scarce, and computations have so far been made for only two glaciers. Calculated and measured annual mass balances showed considerable discrepancies, but their 10-year running means were in reasonable agreement.

CHAPTER 12

GLACIERS AND CLIMATE

"Although the last, not least."

SHAKESPEARE, *King Lear.*

Introduction

The relation between glaciers and climate is a subject of wide-spread interest. The climate, along with the physical properties of ice, ultimately determines the extent and behaviour of glaciers. Moraines and other glacial deposits indicate the limits of glaciers at different times in the past; this is one of the most common bases for inferences about past climates. The relation between glaciers and climate is, however, much more complex than may appear at first sight. We have already dealt with separate aspects of this question; we now want to connect them together.

The problem is in two parts:

(1) How do climatic factors control the glacier's mass balance? This is a question in meteorology.

(2) How does the glacier respond to a change in its mass balance? This is a question in glacier dynamics.

The different steps in the relation between a glacier and the climate can be represented in a "flow chart" such as Fig. 12.1.

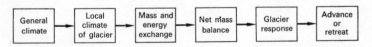

FIG. 12.1. The steps in the relation between the position of a glacier's terminus and the climate. From Meier (1965).

This diagram is oversimplified. There may be other connections: the local climate may change the ice temperature and thereby alter the flow of the glacier without changing its mass balance. There may also be feedback: a glacier can modify its own local climate. The diagram is useful, however: we shall now consider the various stages in it.

The Meteorological Problem

First we explain the distinction between "general" and "local" climate. The "general climate" refers to average conditions over a large area, as indicated, for example, by data from the network of standard weather stations. The "local climate", which may be quite different from the general climate, signifies conditions on the glacier and in its immediate surroundings. Some glaciers owe their existence to peculiarities of local climate. Dolgushin (1961) has pointed out that, in the Polar Urals, the accumulation of wind-blown snow in corries on lee slopes is sufficient to form glaciers, even though the theoretical "snow line" is above the highest summits. Again, some glaciers obtain their main supply from avalanches. Climatic factors influence accumulation on such glaciers only in so far as the size and frequency of avalanches are climatically controlled. Meier (1966) has given the following striking example of two adjacent glaciers with widely different local climates. Klawatti Glacier in northwest U.S.A. consists of two parallel branches of similar size. These join near the terminus but elsewhere are separated by a low rock ridge. The glacier was mapped in 1947 and 1961. Between these dates the thickness of the north branch decreased by an average of 8·3 m while that of the south branch increased by an average of 5·8 m. As these represent differences in the total volumes of the two branches, they cannot merely result from possible differences in response characteristics. Values of accumulation and ablation on the two branches must have differed widely from each other during the period. The two branches must have had different local climates.

Data from distant weather stations are useless for studying local climates. Weather stations in the glacier basin are required; the sites of such stations must be chosen carefully. Automatic

weather stations, which will record standard meteorological parameters and run unattended for several months, are currently
being developed. These should do much to increase our knowledge
of local glacier climates. This aspect of the glacier–climate relationship has hitherto been largely neglected.

The glacier response depends only on the net mass balance, not
on accumulation and ablation separately. However, the climatic
factors which determine accumulation are not the same as those
controlling ablation, and so each must be considered separately.

Many glaciologists have performed statistical analyses relating
accumulation and ablation to climatic parameters. Accumulation
is correlated with precipitation and ablation with mean summer
temperature and with the number of degree-days above 0°C. In
many studies precipitation and temperatures recorded at some
distant weather station have been used, for lack of any measurements at the glacier. Such analyses may have some practical value.
When correlations have been established, the amount of water
stored as snow during the winter and the amount of summer run-
off can perhaps be deduced from the weather records, without any
further measurements on the glacier. However, a correlation
established for one glacier will not necessarily hold in another
area, or even on another glacier in the same area. Moreover, such
analyses tell nothing about the physical factors which control
accumulation and ablation.

Let us examine these factors. Snowfall, blown snow and, in a
few cases, avalanches determine the amount of accumulation.
Refreezing of rain and deposition of rime are seldom important.
The factors which cause ablation vary in importance from place
to place. Calving of icebergs is responsible for the greater part of
the mass loss from the Antarctic ice sheet and for about half the
loss in Greenland. The rate of calving is probably controlled
mainly by oceanographic factors with climate having at most an
indirect influence. Evaporation is often thought to be an important factor in ablation of snow and ice on high mountains, although there are few confirming measurements. In any place
where evaporation is a relatively important cause of ablation, the
total amount of ablation is probably small. With these excep-

tions, melting followed by run-off is the major cause of ablation on glaciers.

In Chapter 4 we described how the heat needed for melting is supplied. In the great majority of heat balance studies it has been found that radiation is the most important source of heat during the ablation season, that more heat is supplied by eddy conduction from the atmosphere than by condensation of atmospheric water vapour, and that the refreezing of rain can be neglected as a heat source (see Table 4.2, page 58).

The amounts of heat supplied by radiation and eddy conduction are not related in any simple way to standard meteorological parameters. For example, it is not the incident radiation but the amount absorbed which is important. Thus the albedo of the surface has a very important influence on the mass balance. Cases have been reported in which deposits of wind-blown dust have substantially increased the ablation. Again, net long-wave radiation depends on both air and surface temperatures. The surface will gain heat from low clouds whose temperature is above 0°C, although normally the long-wave radiation balance is in the opposite direction. Again, whether eddy conduction is an important means of supplying heat at any given time depends on turbulence in the first few metres of air above the surface. Unless warm air is brought in, the air immediately above the surface is soon cooled to the surface temperature and heat transfer by conduction ceases.

The importance of individual climatic parameters varies during the year. In the Arctic, for example, winter air temperatures have little effect on the mass balance. But small differences in summer temperature, which would hardly be noticeable in long-term weather records, may determine whether precipitation falls on the glacier as rain or as snow. A summer snowfall, by increasing the surface albedo, may reduce ablation for several days and so make a considerable difference to the mass balance. In a maritime temperate climate, where summer precipitation is in the form of rain, temperatures in spring and autumn are the most important. As LaChapelle (1965) has pointed out, snowfalls at these times may appreciably shorten the ablation season.

One further complication is a possible positive correlation between mass balance from one year to the next, irrespective of weather conditions. After a year with an abnormally high positive balance there will be firn in some areas where the surface usually consists of ice. At the start of the following summer, the albedo of these areas will be higher than usual. In addition, meltwater which would normally have been lost by run-off over the ice will percolate into the firn and refreeze. Both these factors will tend to increase the mass balance. Again, at the end of a year with an abnormally high negative balance, areas of ice or old firn will be exposed above the normal equilibrium line. In the following year, once the winter's snow has melted, a given amount of incident solar radiation will melt more ice than usual in these areas, as a result of their decreased albedo. This will tend to decrease the mass balance.

To sum up: the micrometeorological problem, that is, what factors determine the amount of accumulation and ablation, is fairly well understood. The factors interact in a complex way, however, and accumulation and ablation cannot be calculated from standard meteorological measurements. Moreover, results obtained on one glacier should not be extrapolated to other glaciers nor even to the same glacier at different times of year. Little is known about the intermediate-scale or meso-meteorological problems: how and to what extent the local climate can differ from one glacier to another, to what extent a glacier can modify its own climate, and how the local climate is related to the general meteorological environment.

The Glacier Response

How a glacier adjusts to a change in its mass balance was discussed in Chapter 11. The glacier response has two important features. First, it introduces a time lag into the system. Secondly, it may introduce an amplification factor: a small change in mass balance can produce a large change at the glacier terminus. Theory has been developed to the point where we can compute how the thickness of a glacier will change in response to a periodic variation of its mass balance. Such a variation can be regarded as one Fourier component of the complex mass balance changes encountered in practice. The theory predicts that, except for very long period variations (of the order of several hundred years), the time lag between maximum (or minimum) mass balance and maximum (or minimum) position of the terminus will be about one quarter of the period. For example, some climatic changes may have a cycle of about 35 years. In such a case, the glacier is expected to reach its greatest extent 9 years after its mass balance was at a maximum. However, it will be much longer, probably a few hundred years, before the adjustment to a particular change is completed.

The two parameters which determine a glacier's response are the kinematic wave velocity, which is roughly four times the ice velocity, and the diffusion coefficient for kinematic waves, which is inversely proportional to the surface slope. Steep, fast-flowing glaciers are expected to react most rapidly. Different values of these parameters can account for differences in behaviour between individual glaciers in the same region, although differences in local climates must also be considered. The theory enables one to separate these two effects, because mass balance changes can be calculated from observed terminal variations. If two glaciers, whose termini are behaving differently, are found to have had similar values of mass balance for the past few tens of years, the difference in behaviour results from a difference in their response characteristics. On the other hand, if their mass balances turn out to have been different from each other, their local climates must also have differed. To make such a calculation requires a considerable amount of data on the geometry, flow, and present mass balance of each glacier however.

One way of bypassing the glacier response problem is to measure mass balance rather than terminus changes. Methods of doing this were described in Chapter 3.

Another method of obtaining information about past climates is to examine cores from the accumulation areas of arctic glaciers. Annual layers can be distinguished in such cores, although in some cases sophisticated methods such as oxygen isotope analyses are needed. In regions where there is no ablation, measurement of the thickness and density of each layer determines the annual precipitation. A core from a region where melting may occur also provides some information about past temperatures: layers with little or no sign of melting indicate relatively cold summers. The classic example of such a study is the analysis of a 411 m core from the Greenland ice sheet (Langway, 1967). The ice at the bottom of this core was deposited as snow about 1000 years ago. Information about past temperatures may also be obtained from measurements of how present temperature varies with depth, as described in Chapter 10.

To draw quantitative inferences about past climates from records of changes in position of a glacier's terminus one would have to trace back through each of the stages in Fig. 12.1. We have seen that this can be done through two stages: mass balance variations can be calculated from measurements of advance and retreat. Quantitative inferences can be carried no further, however, because any given value of mass balance could have resulted from an infinite number of values of accumulation and ablation. There is a similar hiatus at the next stage: weather conditions are not uniquely determined by given values of accumulation and ablation.

Although quantitative deductions are not possible, can we not determine general climatic trends by studying the variations of glacier termini? Even this presents difficulties. To be at all reliable, any such inferences must be based, not on observations on a single glacier, but on a large sample of glaciers in one area. Moreover, one must allow for the time lag in the glacier response, the length of which is uncertain. Some types of glacier should be excluded. Surging glaciers for one; their behaviour is probably unrelated to climatic factors. Glaciers which end in fiords also behave anomalously; their terminal positions are often largely determined by the topography of the fiord.

One example of such a statistical study is that of Hubley (1956) in the Cascade and Olympic Mountains, U.S.A. Many of the glaciers in this area are small, fast-flowing, and fairly steep. Their response times should therefore be relatively short. Between 1953 and 1955, Hubley investigated 73 glaciers. He found that 50 were advancing, 14 others were thickening although their termini had not advanced, and 7 appeared to be stagnant. The condition of the remaining 3 could not be determined. Weather records for the area show a trend, starting about 1943, towards a cooler and wetter climate. Hubley attributed the glacier advances to this.

Detailed observations have been made on at least four glaciers in this area. The behaviour of Nisqually Glacier conforms to the general trend. In 1945 this glacier started to thicken near the equilibrium line (Johnson, 1957). A bulge of increased thickness subsequently moved down the glacier. By 1953, this bulge had formed what was effectively a new active advancing terminus, although some stagnant ice remained further down the valley and continued to melt away. On the other hand, South Cascade Glacier has been retreating for many years (Meier and Tangborn, 1965). Nye (1965b) has computed the mass balance of South Cascade Glacier from measurements of its retreat. The mass balance appears to have been negative, although only slightly so, throughout the 1930's and 1940's. This suggests that the local climate of South Cascade Glacier did not follow the general trend for the area. Klawatti Glacier, mentioned earlier, is also in this area. Between 1947 and 1961 its south branch advanced while its north branch retreated, as a result of peculiarities of the local climate (Meier, 1966). Blue Glacier, in the Olympic Mountains, retreated for about 40 years prior to 1953 and has been more or less stationary since. Its mass balance was strongly negative between 1939 and 1952, and positive from 1952 to 1956 (LaChapelle, 1965). These examples illustrate some of the pitfalls in trying to deduce climatic trends from the behaviour of a single glacier.

Further Reading

There are many papers dealing with aspects of the relation between glaciers and climate, but few which discuss the problem as a whole. Of these few, one might mention articles by Ahlmann (1953), Hoinkes (1964), and Meier (1965).

REFERENCES

THE following special abbreviations are used:

AINA — Arctic Institute of North America, Montreal, Canada.

Antarctic Research — *Antarctic Research*. Geophysical Monograph No. 7 of American Geophysical Union, Washington D.C.

CRREL — U.S. Army Cold Regions Research and Engineering Laboratory, Hanover, New Hampshire.

IASH 47 — International Association of Scientific Hydrology Publication No. 47. (Similarly for other numbers).

Ice and Snow — *Ice and Snow* edited by W. D. Kingery, MIT Press, Cambridge, Mass., U.S.A.

Research in Geophysics 2 — *Research in Geophysics* Vol. 2 edited by H. Odishaw, MIT Press, Cambridge, Mass., U.S.A.

SIPRE — U.S. Army Snow, Ice and Permafrost Research Establishment, Wilmette, Illinois. (The former name for CRREL.)

ADKINS, C. J. (1958) *J. Glaciol.* **3**, 195.

AHLMANN, H. W. (1935a) *Geographical J.* **86**, 97.

AHLMANN, H. W. (1935b) *Geog. Ann.* **17**, 167.

AHLMANN, H. W. (1946) *Geog. Ann.* **28**, 239.

AHLMANN, H. W. (1953) *Glacier Variations and Climatic Fluctuations.* American Geographical Society, New York.

AHLMANN, H. W. and THORARINSSON, S. (1938) *Geog. Ann.* **20**, 171.

ALLEN, C. R., KAMB, W. B., MEIER, M. F. and SHARP, R. P. (1960) *J. Geol.* **68**, 601.

AMBACH, W. (1960) *Archiv für Meteorologie, Geophysik und Bioklimatologie* **10**, 279.

AMBACH, W. and HOINKES, H. (1963) *IASH* **61**, 24.

ANDERSON, D. L. and BENSON, C. S. (1963) *Ice and Snow* 391.

ANDREWS, R. H. (1964) *Meteorology and Heat Balance of the Ablation Area, White Glacier.* Axel Heiberg Island Research Reports, McGill University, Montreal, Canada.

BADER, H. (1960) *SIPRE Research Report* **69**.

BADER, H. (1963) *Ice and Snow* 351.

BENDER, J. A. and GOW, A. J. (1961) *IASH* **55**, 132.

BENSON, C. S. (1961) *Folia Geographica Danica* **9**, 13.

BENTLEY, C. R. (1964) *Research in Geophysics 2*, 335.

BODVARSSON, G. (1955) *Jökull* **5**, 1.

BOGOSLOVSKI, V. N. (1958) *IASH* **47**, 287.

BOURGOIN, J.-P. (1956) *Annales de Géophysique* **12**, 75.

BULL, C. (1956) *Geographical J.* **122**, 219.

BULL, C. (1957) *J. Glaciol.* **3**, 67.

BUTKOVICH, T. R. and LANDAUER, J. K. (1960) *SIPRE Research Report* **72**.

CAMERON, R. L. and BULL, C. B. (1962) *Antarctic Research* 178.

CAROL, H. (1947) *J. Glaciol.* **1**, 57.

CARSLAW, H. S. and JAEGER, J. C. (1959) *Conduction of Heat in Solids* (2nd edition). Clarendon, Oxford, England.

COLLINS, I. F. (1968) *J. Glaciol.* in press.

CORBATO, C. E. (1965) *J. Glaciol.* **5**, 637.

COSTES, N. C. (1963) *Ice and Snow* 412.

CRARY, A. P. (1960) *Arctic* **13**, 32.

DESIO, A. (1954) *J. Glaciol.* **2**, 383.

DIAMOND, M. (1960) *J. Glaciol.* **3**, 558.

DOELL, R. R. (1963) *J. Glaciol.* **4**, 425.

DOLGUSHIN, L. D. (1961) *IASH* **54**, 335.

DOLGUSHIN, L. D., YEVTEYEV, S. A., KOTLYAKOV, Y. M. (1962) *IASH* **58**, 286.

DOLGUSHIN, L. D., YEVTEYEV, S. A., KRENKE, A. N., ROTOTAYEV, K. G. and SVATKOV, N. M. (1963) *Priroda* **11**, 85. (In Russian. English translation by E. R. Hope, Defence Research Board of Canada Translation T409R.)

ERIKSSON, B. E. (1942) *Geog. Ann.* **24**, 23.

EVANS, S. (1963) *Polar Record* **11**, 406.

EVISON, F. F. (1960) *Geophysical J.* **3**, 155.

FINSTERWALDER, R. (1959) *J. Glaciol.* **3**, 547 (letter).

FISHER, J. E. (1963) *J. Glaciol.* **4**, 513.

GERRARD, J. A. F., PERUTZ, M. F. and ROCH, A. (1952) *Proc. Roy. Soc.* **A213**, 546.

GLEN, A. R. (1941) *Geographical J.* **98**, 206.

GLEN, J. W. (1954) *J. Glaciol.* **2**, 316.

GLEN, J. W. (1955) *Proc. Roy. Soc.* **A228**, 519.

GLEN, J. W. (1958a) *Advances in Physics* **7**, 254.

GLEN, J. W. (1958b) *IASH* **47**, 171.

GLEN, J. W. (1963a) *Ice and Snow* 3.

GLEN, J. W. (1963b) *Bulletin of IASH* **8**, 2, 68 (contribution to discussion).

GLEN, J. W. and JONES, S. J. (1968) *Proceedings of Conference on Physics of Snow and Ice*, Hokkaido University, Japan, 1966. In press.

GOLD, L. W. (1963) *Ice and Snow* 8.

GOLDTHWAIT, R. P. (1960) *SIPRE Technical Report* **39**.

GOW, A. J. (1963a) *IASH* **61**, 272.

GOW, A. J. (1963b) *J. Glaciol.* **4**, 771.

GRAINGER, M. E. and LISTER, H. (1966) *J. Glaciol.* **6**, 101.

GREENHOUSE, J. P. (1961) *Arctic* **14**, 259.

HAEFELI, R. (1951) *J. Glaciol.* **1**, 496.

HAEFELI, R. (1961) *J. Glaciol.* **3**, 1133.

HAEFELI, R. and BRENTANI, F. (1955) *J. Glaciol.* **2**, 571.

HANSEN, B. L. and LANDAUER, J. K. (1958) *IASH* **47**, 313.

HANSEN, B. L. and LANGWAY, C. C. (1966) *Antarctic J. of the U.S.* **1**, 207.

HATTERSLEY-SMITH, G. (1963) *J. Glaciol.* **4**, 415.

HATTERSLEY-SMITH, G. (1964) *Nature* **201**, 176.

HAVENS, J. M. (1964) *Meteorology and Heat Balance of the Accumulation Area, McGill Ice Cap.* Axel Heiberg Island Research Reports, McGill University, Montreal, Canada.

HAVENS, J. M., MÜLLER, F. and WILMOT, G. C. (1965) *Comparative Meteorological Survey and a Short-term Heat Balance Study of the White Glacier.* Axel Heiberg Island Research Reports, McGill University, Montreal, Canada.

HOBBS, P. V. (1965) *J. Geophys. Res.* **70**, 3903.

HOBBS, P. V. and MASON, B. J. (1964) *Phil. Mag.* **9**, 181.

HOINKES, H. (1953) *Geog. Ann.* **35**, 116.

HOINKES, H. (1955) *J. Glaciol.* **2**, 497.

HOINKES, H. C. (1964) *Research in Geophysics 2*, 391.

HOINKES, H. and RUDOLPH, R. (1962a) *J. Glaciol.* **4**, 266.

HOINKES, H. and RUDOLPH, R. (1962b) *IASH* **58**, 16.

HOINKES, H. and UNTERSTEINER, N. (1952) *Geog. Ann.* **34**, 99.

HOLTZSCHERER, J. J. and BAUER, A. (1954) *IASH* **39**, 244.

HUBLEY, R. C. (1956) *J. Glaciol.* **2**, 669.

HUGHES, T. P. and SELIGMAN, G. (1938) *Mon. Not. Roy. Astr. Soc. Geophys. Supp.* **4**, 616.

IMBERT, B. (1959) *Geophysical J.* **2**, 164 (contribution to discussion).

JAEGER, J. C. (1962) *Elasticity, Fracture and Flow* (2nd edition). Methuen, London, England.

JENSSEN, D. and RADOK, U. (1961) *IASH* **55**, 112.

JENSSEN, D. and RADOK, U. (1963) *J. Glaciol.* **4**, 387.

JOHNSON, A. (1957) *J. Glaciol.* **3**, 50.

KAMB, W. B. (1961) *J. Glaciol.* **3**, 1097.

KAMB, B. and LACHAPELLE, E. (1964) *J. Glaciol.* **5**, 159.

KAMB, W. B. and SHREVE, R. L. (1963) *Trans. of Amer. Geophys. Un.* **44**, 103. (abstract only)

KAPITSA, A. P. (1964) *Soviet Antarctic Exped. Info. Bull.* **1**, 25. (English translation published by Elsevier, Amsterdam, Holland. Date of original paper is 1958.)

KEELER, C. M. (1964) *AINA Research Paper* **27**.

KOTLYAKOV, V. M. (1961) *IASH* **55**, 100.

KRENKE, A. N. (1963) *Bull. of IASH* **8**, 2, 94 (contribution to discussion).

LACHAPELLE, E. (1959a) *J. Glaciol.* **3**, 458.

LACHAPELLE, E. R. (1959b) *J. Geophys. Res.* **64**, 443.

LACHAPELLE, E. (1960) *The Blue Glacier Project.* Report from Dept. of Meteorology and Climatology, University of Washington, Seattle, U.S.A.

238   REFERENCES

LACHAPELLE, E. (1961) *IASH* **54**, 302.
LACHAPELLE, E. (1962) *J. Glaciol.* **4**, 290.
LACHAPELLE, E. (1965) *J. Glaciol.* **5**, 609.
LANGWAY, C. C. (1958) *SIPRE Technical Report* **62**.
LANGWAY, C. C. (1967) *CRREL Research Report* **77**.
LEBEDEVA, I. M. (1960) *Glaciological Researches* **5**, 117. (Section IX of IGY Programme, Acad. Sci. U.S.S.R., Moscow.)
LIGHTHILL, M. J. and WHITHAM, G. B. (1955) *Proc. Roy. Soc.* **A229**, 281.
LILJEQUIST, G. H. (1957) *Norwegian–British–Swedish Antarctic Expedition 1949-52, Scientific Results*, Vol. 2, Pt. 1. Norsk Polarinstitutt, Oslo.
LISTER, H. (1959) *Geophys. J.* **2**, 164 (contribution to discussion).
LISTER, H. (1962) *AINA Research Paper* **19**.
LISTER, H. and TAYLOR, P. F. (1961) *Meddelelser om Grønland* **158**, 7, 1.
LLIBOUTRY, L. (1958a) *IASH* **47**, 125.
LLIBOUTRY, L. (1958b) *J. Glaciol.* **3**, 261.
LLIBOUTRY, L. (1963) *Bull of IASH* **8**, 2, 82 (contribution to discussion).
LLIBOUTRY, L. (1964) *Traité de Glaciologie* Tome 1. Masson, Paris.
LLIBOUTRY, L. (1965) *Traité de Glaciologie* Tome 2. Masson, Paris.
LLIBOUTRY, L. (1966) *J. Geophys. Res.* **71**, 2535.
LOEWE, F. (1966) *J. Glaciol.* **6**, 179 (letter).
MATHEWS, W. H. (1959) *J. Glaciol.* **3**, 448.
MATHEWS, W. H. (1963) *IASH* **63**, 290.
MATHEWS, W. H. (1964) *J. Glaciol.* **5**, 235.
McCALL, J. G. (1952) *J. Glaciol.* **2**, 122.
MEIER, M. F. (1960) *U.S. Geol. Surv. Professional Paper* **351**.
MEIER, M. F. (1965) In *The Quaternary of the United States* edited by H. E. Wright and D. G. Frey, Princeton University Press, Princeton, New Jersey, 795.
MEIER, M. F. (1966) *Canadian J. of Earth Sciences* **3**, 811.
MEIER, M. F. (1967) *A Proposal for Mass Balance Terms*. Part of a draft manual prepared for International Hydrological Decade.
MEIER, M. F., CAMPBELL, W. J., TANGBORN, W. V. and POST, A. (1966) *Ice* **22**, 7.
MEIER, M. F. and JOHNSON, J. N. (1962) *J. Geophys. Res.* **67**, 886. (abstract only).
MEIER, M. F. and POST, A. S. (1962) *IASH* **58**, 63.
MEIER, M. F. and TANGBORN, W. V. (1961) *U.S. Geol. Surv. Professional Paper* **424B**, 14.
MEIER, M. F. and TANGBORN, W. V. (1965) *J. Glaciol.* **5**, 547.
MELLOR, M. (1960) *J. Glaciol.* **3**, 773.
MILLER, M. M. (1958) *J. Glaciol.* **3**, 293.
MOCK, S. J. (1966) *J. Glaciol.* **6**, 369.
MUGURUMA, J., MAE, S. and HIGASHI, A. (1966) *Phil. Mag.* **13**, 625.
MÜLLER, F. (1962a) *J. Glaciol.* **4**, 302.
MÜLLER, F. (1962b) *IASH* **58**, 131.

MÜLLER, F. (1963) *IASH* **61**, 168.

NYE, J. F. (1951) *Proc. Roy. Soc.* **A207**, 554.

NYE, J. F. (1952a) *J. Glaciol.* **2**, 82.

NYE, J. F. (1952b) *J. Glaciol.* **2**, 103.

NYE, J. F. (1955) *J. Glaciol.* **2**, 512 (letter).

NYE, J. F. (1957) *Proc. Roy. Soc.* **A239**, 113.

NYE, J. F. (1958) *Nature* **181**, 1450.

NYE, J. F. (1959a) *J. Glaciol.* **3**, 409.

NYE, J. F. (1959b) *J. Glaciol.* **3**, 493.

NYE, J. F. (1960) *Proc. Roy. Soc.* **A256**, 559.

NYE, J. F. (1961) *IASH* **54**, 397.

NYE, J. F. (1963a) *Geophysical J.* **7**, 431.

NYE, J. F. (1963b) *Proc. Roy. Soc.* **A275**, 87.

NYE, J. F. (1965a) *J. Glaciol.* **5**, 661.

NYE, J. F. (1965b) *J. Glaciol.* **5**, 589.

NYE, J. F. (1965c) *J. Glaciol.* **5**, 567.

OROWAN, E. (1949) *J. Glaciol.* **1**, 231.

ORVIG, S. (1954) *Geog. Ann.* **36**, 193.

POST, A. S. (1960) *J. Geophys. Res.* **65**, 3703.

POST, A. S. (1965) *Science* **148**, 366.

POST, A. S. (1966) *J. Glaciol.* **6**, 375.

POST, A. S. (1967) *J. Glaciol.* **6**, 763 (letter).

POUNDER, E. R. (1965) *The Physics of Ice.* Pergamon Press, Oxford, England.

PYTTE, R. and ØSTREM, G. (1965) *Norges Vassdrags- og Elektrisitetsvesen, Meddelelse fra Hydrologisk Avdeling* **14**, 1.

RARATY, L. E. and TABOR, D. (1958) *Proc. Roy. Soc.* **A245**, 184.

RIGSBY, G. P. (1958) *J. Glaciol.* **3**, 273.

RIGSBY, G. P. (1960) *J. Glaciol.* **3**, 589.

ROBIN, G. DE Q. (1955) *J. Glaciol.* **2**, 523.

ROBIN, G. DE Q. (1958) *Norwegian–British–Swedish Antarctic Expedition 1949-52, Scientific Results,* Vol. 5. Norsk Polarinstitutt, Oslo.

ROBIN, G. DE Q. (1967) *Nature* **215**, 1029.

ROBINSON, E. S. (1966) *J. Glaciol.* **6**, 43.

SAGAR, R. B. (1966) *Geographical Bull.* **8**, 3.

SAVAGE, J. C. and PATERSON, W. S. B. (1963) *J. Geophys. Res.* **68**, 4521.

SAVAGE, J. C. and PATERSON, W. S. B. (1965) *J. Geophys. Res.* **70**, 3511 (letter).

SCHYTT, V. (1955) *SIPRE Report* **28**.

SCHYTT, V. (1962) *J. Glaciol.* **4**, 281.

SCHYTT, V. (1964) *Geog. Ann.* **46**, 243.

SELIGMAN, G. (1936) *Snow Structure and Ski Fields.* Macmillan, London, England.

SESHU, S. and BALABANIAN, N. (1959) *Linear Network Analysis.* Wiley, New York, U.S.A.

SHARP, R. P. (1951) *J. Geol.* **59**, 599.

SHARP, R. P. (1953) *J. Glaciol.* **2**, 182.

SHARP, R. P. (1960) *Glaciers.* University of Oregon Press, Eugene, Oregon, U.S.A.

SHREVE, R. L. (1961) *IASH* **54**, 530.

SHUMSKIY, P. A. (1958) *IASH* **47**, 244.

SHUMSKIY, P. A. (1964) *Principles of Structural Glaciology.* English translation by D. Kraus, Dover, New York, U.S.A.

SHUMSKIY, P. A., KRENKE, A. N. and ZOTIKOV, I. A. (1964) *Research in Geophysics* **2**, 425.

SKEIB, G. (1962) *Zeitschrift für Meteorologie* **16**, 1.

SMITH, J. (1960) *J. Glaciol.* **3**, 707.

SORGE, E. (1933) *Geographical J.* **81**, 333.

STEINEMANN, S. (1954) *IASH* **39**, 449.

STEINEMANN, S. (1958a) *IASH* **47**, 184.

STEINEMANN, S. (1958b) *Beiträge zur Geologie der Schweiz, Hydrologie* 10.

SVERDRUP, H. V. (1935a) *Geog. Ann.* **17**, 53.

SVERDRUP, H. V. (1935b) *Geog. Ann.* **17**, 145.

TANGBORN, W. V. (1966) *Water Resources Research* **2**, 105.

TARR, R. S. and MARTIN, L. (1914) *Alaskan Glacier Studies.* National Geographic Society, Washington D.C.

TIEN, C. (1960) *SIPRE Research Report* **64**.

VIALOV, S. S. (1958) *IASH* **47**, 266.

VILESOV, Y. N. (1961) *IASH* **54**, 313.

VOYTKOVSKIY, K. F. (1960) *Mechanical Properties of Ice.* Publishing House of the Academy of Sciences of the U.S.S.R. (In Russian).

WALLEN, C. C. (1948) *Geog. Ann.* **30**, 451.

WARD, W. H. and ORVIG, S. (1953) *J. Glaciol.* **2**, 158.

WEBB, W. W. and HAYES, C. E. (1967) *Phil. Mag.* **16**, 909.

WEERTMAN, J. (1955) *J. App. Phys.* **26**, 1213.

WEERTMAN, J. (1957a) *J. Glaciol.* **3**, 33.

WEERTMAN, J. (1957b) *J. Glaciol.* **3**, 38.

WEERTMAN, J. (1957c) *J. App. Phys.* **28**, 362.

WEERTMAN, J. (1957d) *J. App. Phys.* **28**, 1185.

WEERTMAN, J. (1958) *IASH* **47**, 162.

WEERTMAN, J. (1961a) *J. Glaciol.* **3**, 953.

WEERTMAN, J. (1961b) *J. Glaciol.* **3**, 965.

WEERTMAN, J. (1961c) *J. Geophys. Res.* **66**, 3783.

WEERTMAN, J. (1962a) *IASH* **58**, 31.

WEERTMAN, J. (1962b) *J. Geophys. Res.* **67**, 1133.

WEERTMAN, J. (1963) *Ice and Snow* 28.

WEERTMAN, J. (1964) *J. Glaciol.* **5**, 287.

WEERTMAN, J. (1967) *J. Glaciol.* **6**, 489.

WEERTMAN, J. (1968) *J. Geophys. Res.* in press.

WEERTMAN, J. and WEERTMAN, J. R. (1964) *Elementary Dislocation Theory.* Macmillan, New York, U.S.A.

WEXLER, H. (1959) *J. Glaciol.* **3**, 420.

WEXLER, H. (1960) *J. Glaciol.* **3,** 626.
WEXLER, H. (1961) *J. Glaciol.* **3,** 1075.
ZOTIKOV, I. A. (1963) *Bull. of IASH* **8,** 1, 36.
ZUMBERGE, J. H. and SWITHINBANK, C. (1962) *Antarctic Research* 197.

SUBJECT INDEX

GEOGRAPHIC INDEX

DATE DUE

GAYLORD			PRINTED IN U.S.A.